THE DELTIC LOCOMOTIVES
OF BRITISH RAIL

Brian Webb

DAVID & CHARLES
Newton Abbot   London   North Pomfret (Vt)

The changing order – D9003 *Meld* at King's Cross in 1961 overshadows Class A4 Pacific 60028 *Walter K. Whigham* on the down Elizabethan. (*Brian Webb collection*)

CONTENTS

British Library Cataloguing in Publication Data

Webb, Brian
    The Deltic locomotives of British Rail.
    1. Diesel locomotives – Great Britain
    I. Title
    385′.3662′0941   TJ619

    ISBN 0–7153–8110–5

Photoset by
Northern Phototypesetting Co. Bolton
and printed in Great Britain
by Biddles Ltd. Guildford Surrey
for David & Charles (Publishers) Limited
Brunel House Newton Abbot Devon

Published in the United States of America
by David & Charles Inc.
North Pomfret Vermont 05053 USA

INTRODUCTION AND ACKNOWLEDGEMENTS

This book has been written following original research and with the kind co-operation of British Rail Eastern Region, which provided access to official documentation, and of GEC Traction Ltd, which permitted research into the surviving records of the English Electric Deltic locomotives.

Since I wrote *English Electric Mainline Diesel Locomotives of British Rail* (David & Charles 1976) more material has become available, although I have tried to avoid repeating much of what has been published previously. The book aims to extend and complete the story so far as possible in the final phase of the life of the Deltic locomotives, and I have attempted to include all aspects of the subject deemed important. It is unfortunate that not all the documentation of the 1955 prototype Deltic has survived, presumably having been lost or destroyed.

Excesses of technical detail and intricacy have hopefully been avoided and the approach is basically factual, relating to design, delivery, operational problems and their rectification, all three types of Deltic-engined locomotive being covered. The majority of the material has not been made public before, and it is hoped that the reader may gain some further insight into these remarkable locomotives.

I would like to thank British Rail Eastern Region and its Chief Mechanical & Electrical Engineer's staff at York, notably Irving Wells, Engineering Assistant, David F. Russell, Mechanical & Electrical Engineer (Locomotives), F. J. H. Chapman, Senior Clerk, Rolling Stock Statistics Section, and H. Lillford, Assistant, Rolling Stock Statistics, for their help. The assistance of GEC Traction Ltd enables me to say a special 'thank you' to Mike Scott, Assistant Marketing Manager, and his secretary, Mrs Connie Finnigan. A number of strings have been pulled at GEC Traction for the benefit of research and I acknowledge this most gratefully.

To my long-standing friend, Allan C. Baker, Depot Engineer, Finsbury Park Traction Maintenance Depot, his 'Deltic racehorses', and helpful comments, together with Dennis Edwards, Engineering Assistant, King's Cross, further thanks are duly recorded.

Other assistance has come from E. G. M. Wilkes, Ken Hoole, members and officers of the Deltic Preservation Society, the Diesel & Electric Group, the Stephenson Locomotive Society, The Railway Correspondence & Travel Society; to these and many others who have unwittingly contributed to the book during discussions, thank you.

Illustrations other than those from my own collection have been furnished by GEC Traction Ltd, GEC Diesels Ltd, J. F. Aylard, Allan C. Baker, Brian Lee, E. G. M. Wilkes, Roger Newling-Goode, G. F. Bannister, Roland Hummerston, H. L. Holland, David Sharp, Iain M. Flynn, Dr Les Nixon, Les Bertram, and D. A. Idle. Backstage assistance with illustrations and photographic work has come from Alan Simpson, and J. Robin Lidster.

The manuscript was prepared and typed by Sandra J. C. Tassell, to whom once again I am indebted for her interest and care, and who is beginning to understand my obsession with diesel and electric locomotives, particularly the Deltics.

BRIAN WEBB

Publisher's note

Hardly had the manuscript of this book been received in the publisher's office when the sad news came of the death of the author. It was the wish of his family that publication should continue and this book stands as a tribute to Brian Webb.

CHAPTER 1

THE PROTOTYPE DELTIC LOCOMOTIVE

Design work for the prototype *Deltic* locomotive began at the Preston works of The English Electric Co Ltd (EE) during September 1951 under the job name of "Enterprise" and also coded DP1 (Diesel Prototype No 1), *Enterprise* to be the name bestowed on the finished locomotive. The subsequent abandonment of the name was due to the introduction of a new range of diesel-mechanical locomotives by the Leeds-based locomotive builder, Hudswell, Clarke & Co Ltd, the first example of which was also named *Enterprise*, the range being rigid-frame in design and embodying the so-called Paxman constant-horsepower diesel engine.

The Deltic locomotive was actually ordered by EE Traction Division at Bradford from EE Preston works on 20 November 1951 under contract No. 6B2000. At the same time various components and items of equipment were also ordered: nine, later reduced to seven, traction motors; three main and auxiliary generators; three exhausters; two air compressors; five traction motor blowers; one set of control equipment; three complete bogies, later reduced to two, with sufficient spares to effect a quick repair; one train-heating steam generator (SG); one complete locomotive set of radiators and fans, plus associated equipment. The extra items of equipment in the orders were to provide spares. Many smaller items were also ordered.

The Deltic diesel engines were ordered on 10 September 1951, three being required, giving one spare, but on the 27th of the month the order was cancelled as Napier wished to supply these as a private venture free of charge. The first two engines were expected to be ready by September 1952 and the third one month later. The whole of the cost of the Deltic project was borne by EE and set against development work.

The evolution of the Deltic locomotive was one involving much revision and compromise, and even when construction was under way at Preston modifications were made to suit day-to-day requirements, it being said that the mechanical parts had so many variations from the drawing that it would have been impossible to repeat the

locomotive should the need have arisen!

Mechanically, the locomotive was not unusual. There was a substantial underframe which was lowered between the bogies to provide increased interior height, and based on rolled-steel channels with flanged girders for the centre longitudinals, with cross-members and reinforced ends for the buffing and drawgear. The underframe was decked over with plate and was oil-tight. The superstructure was built up on the underframe, apart from the nose and cab frame units which were built on the shop floor. Rolled-steel sections were used for framing and the body panelling attached by welding. A lot of light alloy components were employed to keep down weight, *ie* roof sections, doors, louvres, treadplates, conduit, ducting and pipework. The general construction can be seen in the illustrations provided.

Fabricated steel bogies with box-section side members were used with the transoms, and headstocks, suitably gusseted for strength, riveted to them. Brackets for traction motor suspension on the transoms were designed for easy removal, allowing the complete motor and wheelset to be dropped out. The bogie bolster was fabricated and had rubber pads set in the side bearers to insulate as far as possible against vibration and sound transmission.

Cooling air for the traction motors was passed through the hollow bogie centre into the bolster and thence through leather bellows connected to the motors. Forged steel equalising beams of straight 'I' section to reduce unsprung weight were carried in stirrups incorporated in the roller-bearing axleboxes. Solid disc type wheels were fitted.

The locomotive was completed and moved by road to the EE works at Netherton, Liverpool; at that time it was nameless and kept hidden from public view until it completed its initial static testing schedules. The rather flamboyant and garish powder-blue livery with aluminium mouldings on the bodysides, plus bright yellow chevrons or 'speed-whiskers' on its nose fronts, was certainly to prove good for publicity when it

The world's then most powerful single-unit diesel locomotive. The 3300hp prototype *Deltic* without its name, photographed during 1955 at the English Electric Co. Netherton Works, Liverpool, where it did its early static tests. (*Brian Webb collection*)

did appear in public. Its original livery before leaving Preston was the traditional EE green-and-cream 'house colour'. This scheme, it is said, was replaced following adverse comments from Lady Nelson who evidently likened its appearance to an electric cooker, and suggested the alternative livery.

When *Deltic* started work on the LMR in the autumn of 1955, it was mostly under the cover of darkness on freight trains between Liverpool and London, continuing this work for some ten months to enable running experience and development work to be completed. Its first passenger working was apparently on the up Merseyside Express returning with the down Shamrock to Liverpool on 13 December 1955.

At this time − indeed for most of its period on the LMR − *Deltic* was based at Speke Junction shed so that easy access was possible to Netherton works and later Vulcan Foundry (VF) for maintenance or repairs.

Much static testing was undertaken in late 1955, followed by braking and wheelslip checks at Speke, then by Edge Hill-Preston runs with empty coaching stock (ECS) trains and static tests of the train-heating steam generator, with up to 20 carriages, at Edge Hill, during which the Deltic diesel engines were running at idling speeds for up to two hours continuously.

On 28 November 1955 the locomotive began work on alternate nights with an express freight between Edge Hill and Camden Town, London, leaving Edge Hill at 19.30hrs and arriving Camden at 03.07hrs, the locomotive stabling at Willesden shed until returning north at 19.35hrs, to arrive Edge Hill at 01.07hrs, before being stabled at Speke. By this time the locomotive's engines had run for 387 hours and 399 hours respectively, of which 164 hours and 148 hours had been on British Rail. During the period 12 March to 29 September 1956 the locomotive put in 91 days running out of 96 days when it was available for service, and had two periods totalling 69 days in Netherton works for modifications.

The locomotive was originally designed to operate with both diesel engines running, other than in an emergency. Changing of the transmission characteristics to suit the reduced power available from one-engine operation was not originally provided for, and the connection of the auxiliary loading resulted in auxiliary equipment such as traction motor blowers operating at about half their designed speed.

Experience indicated that in some instances one-engine operation was more economical, and the locomotive was modified to permit this with all equipment and all six traction motors working normally. With only half-voltage available, the traction motor field-divert resistances were altered to give a top speed of 75mph with a reasonable weight of train. The necessary switching was interlocked with the main generator cut-out switches providing automatic circuit changing. Major alterations to the auxiliary circuitry was done to enable all four traction motor blowers to be fed from either auxiliary generator.

During the period in late 1955 when the locomotive was operating on fitted freights and the diesel engines were only lightly loaded, they operated with dirty exhausts in the low rpm idling speed range, causing carbon build-up and the emission of sparks when power was applied. The original pistons had too much clearance for traction use, and these were replaced by pistons with reduced clearance and modified oil-scraper arrangements, giving some improvement, although by no means curing the problem. Development of a new piston with a different combustion chamber was proved on the test bed and subsequently fitted to the locomotive's engines, giving a pronounced improvement in exhaust quality.

During early trials the engines had a tendency to stall when they were throttled back rapidly. This was due to temporary overloading caused by the delay in reduction of the generator field by the load regulator. Minor modifications to the main generator field resistance circuits and controller air valves solved this.

The wheelslip protection system proved to be

too sensitive and gave warning of slip when none took place. This was corrected.

Deltic was designed for a maximum speed of 90mph, which was found too low, so the gear ratio of the traction motors was changed from 61:19 to 59:21 giving a top speed of 105mph; the redundant gears and pinions were interestingly re-used on Class 40 locomotives D200–D209.

Other problems included gear-case fatigue fractures at around 180,000 miles of running; stronger cases and high-tensile steel bolts were fitted. The solid disc wheels gave trouble at around 12,500 miles due to shelling of the treads. It was thought that the non-ferrous brake blocks and their thermal effects when braking were to blame, so following wheel turning cast-iron blocks were fitted, but without improvement. The locomotive subsequently required further wheel-turning and then settled down to run another 105,000 miles without further attention. No solution to the shelling problem emerged.

Although noted for good riding, a certain amount of vertical oscillation was recorded at 12mph and 52mph, which led to the fitting of four hydraulic shock absorbers to each bogie between the equalising beams and the bogie frames.

After about 200 hours of static engine test running, fatigue cracking occurred in the engine air ducting, its filters, and the locomotive body side. Vibrations of the locomotive superstructure and diesel engine pulsations were the cause, and although strengthening was carried out, the problem continued when the locomotive was in service. This was so severe that on two occasions pieces of fractured ducting were sucked into the engines, causing failure. The problem became so

Cut-away drawing of prototype *Deltic*. (*GEC Diesels Ltd*)

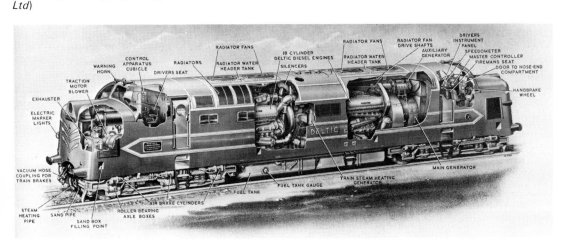

Completed underframe of prototype *Deltic* at the English Electric Preston works in 1954. The lowered centre section can be seen, and a traction motor blower mounted at front right-hand side of the frame. (*GEC Traction Ltd*)

critical that the ducting was taken out and the engine air drawn straight from the engine room, which in turn made the engine room very warm and created air pulsations, upsetting the performance of the train-heating steam generator. Ducting of a new design was fitted and operated satisfactorily.

During the period August to September 1956 a comprehensive test programme evolved by EE and BR was undertaken on the Settle and Carlisle line between Carlisle and Skipton, using the LMR dynamometer car and two mobile testing units. The tests were to establish the locomotive's power output, fuel consumption, and prove EE theoretical performance calculations. The whole of the results of the test programme can be found in the British Transport Commission (BTC) Performance and Efficiency Test Bulletin No 19, published in September 1956. The report included the following points:

The programme tested the power outputs obtainable with one and two engines running, using four different controller settings, giving engine speeds of 800, 900, 1200 and 1500rpm;

and eight settings with two engines running, including the above settings plus 700, 1050, 1300 and 1400rpm. 700rpm represented engine idling speed and 1500rpm engine full power.

A maximum drawbar tractive effort (TE) of 45,550lb was sustained for two minutes without slipping, representing an adhesion factor of 19%. This TE was just below the operation limit of the overload relays of 2700A, the locomotive's current ratings being 2700A maximum, twenty minutes at 2000A, and 1650A continuously. These corresponded to drawbar TE of 46,200lb at 19·5mph, 31,500lb at 31mph and 24,500 lb at 41·5mph.

When working at maximum engine power the bhp was 3250 and rail hp constant at 2650, or 81% of the bhp, the 19% loss being due to 5% auxiliaries, 6% main generator, and 8% traction motors. Maximum drawbar horsepower (dbhp) at constant speed on the level was 2580 at 40mph, falling to 2410 hp at 70mph, with corresponding thermal efficiencies of 27·5% and 25·7% respectively.

To prove the locomotive's performance characteristics obtained with the test train, a load of 642 tons (20 coaches) was hauled by *Deltic* working at maximum power. The locomotive sustained an almost constant dbhp

Superstructure frame of prototype *Deltic* at Preston works. Apart from some variations in nose and bodyside contours, the design is similar to that used for Class 55. (*GEC Traction Ltd*)

of 2200 for long periods, and on the 15 miles of 1 in 100 between Ormside and Ais Gill average speed was 56mph, and not once did this fall below 50mph.

Working with only one engine at maximum power the dbhp varied from 1270 at 25mph to 1100 at 60mph, which due to locomotive resistance and auxiliary power absorbing a greater proportion of bhp than with both engines working, and with the traction motors less efficient due to operation at half voltage, was considerably less than half of the power produced by both engines working. It was possible to get the same maximum TE with one engine as with two, but at reduced speed.

The locomotive was reported to have covered some 5000 miles during the tests and been remarkably trouble-free, without any significant mechanical, engine, or electrical problems. The engines had proved smooth-running and vibration-free, although noisy when idling, being particularly objectionable when standing in stations. On one run two traction motors flashed-over when deliberately overloaded during wheelslip tests.

Conclusions after the tests indicated that the locomotive was capable of taking 500 tons over Shap at 41mph. During the tests the locomotive and its test train were based at Carlisle Durranhill shed.

From October 1956 *Deltic* was mainly on Edge Hill–Preston empty coaching stock duties, prior to taking on Liverpool–Euston workings during the 26 October to 29 December period. It began Anglo-Scottish workings between Euston and Carlisle on 31 December, stabling at Carlisle Upperby and refuelling at Kingmoor, continuing this work until 9 March 1957 when it entered Netherton works, remaining there until 13 May. Returning to Liverpool–Euston workings on 15 May, this duty continued until 31 December 1958.

On the Euston–Carlisle duties the locomotive took loads of between 382 and 669 tons, and test records show that in the week ending 3 March 1957 Deltic ran 3663 miles at an overall engine fuel consumption of 1.85 gal per 1000 gross ton miles. During June 1957 EE considered that the locomotive was now in full service, it being exhibited at a rolling stock exhibition at Battersea Wharf from 21 June to 2 July 1957.

Recorded defects at the time included cracked

The locomotive that the London Midland Region did not want – *Deltic* on controlled road testing during August and September 1956 with dynamometer car and two mobile test units on the Settle & Carlisle line just south of Armathwaite. (*GEC Traction Ltd*)

air ducting, broken coolant pipes, failed traction motor blowers, main generator defects, flat batteries, and following boiler failures, the experimental fitting for a 3-month period of a Clayton train-heating steam generator which EE was planning to build under licence. Exchange of the engines coincided with a decision to order a fourth spare Deltic engine and its generator group for delivery by the end of 1957.

On 3 December *Deltic* worked a special Canadian trade mission train from Euston to Glasgow and back. On 20 December the locomotive's mileage was stated to be 254,703. *Deltic* was never stretched on the LMR, although some of its daily mileages exceeded 700, and one cannot help thinking that the Midland Railway 'small engine' policy still commanded respect, for the LMR never realised the potential of the locomotive as a traffic machine.

During the period up to the end of 1958 there were a number of visits to Netherton works and from May of that year to VF, its first visit being for repairs, including a complete overhaul.

The ER had been seeking to try the locomotive for some time and it was duly delivered to that region during week ending 18 January 1959. It was based at Hornsey depot and was immediately dogged by route and loading gauge restrictions. While on the ER it was arranged that Stratford would undertake repair work under EE supervision to avoid running via the LMR to VF, although periodic visits were made there.

Initial test running took it to York, Leeds, Doncaster and Newcastle, and on freight train trials to Doncaster. On a run to Newcastle *Deltic* took a 350-ton load at a speed and timing which almost equalled the pre-war Silver Jubilee timing. Due to severe loading gauge clearance problems north of York the locomotive was mainly operated between King's Cross and Doncaster.

For test running on the Scottish Region from Edinburgh, the locomotive had to work from Euston to Carlisle on 8 June 1959 and then run light via the Waverley line, trials starting from Edinburgh on the 9th with light engine running to Berwick and Glasgow Cowlairs. On the next three days it worked Craigentinny–Glasgow and also Edinburgh–Berwick passenger duties. Some days the locomotive was not used, but other days saw it on Slateford–Carlisle runs, before it finally came back via the Waverley line and the LMR light engine to Willesden on 18 June, returning to the ER which put it on Doncaster and Leeds workings. On 4 July 1959 its cumulative mileage was 288,392.

Deltic was to continue on the ER until March

1961, during which time the following defects were recorded: derailment damage; train-heating equipment failures; engine failures and engine changing; radiator cleaning and maintenance, which kept the locomotive at Stratford from 20 April to 29 May 1959; defective tyres – locomotive at VF 14 July to 25 August 1959; governor defects; No 1 scavenge-blower failure; dirty main generator field contactors; voltage regulator; vacuum exhauster problems; fractured lubricating oil pipe; engine decarbonising and injector testing; earth faults; flat batteries; load regulator control circuit defects; engine changing; piston seizure; connecting rod fracture; crankcase fracture on No 1 engine; brake gear; worn traction motor brushes.

On 11 May 1960 the locomotive was withdrawn and sent to VF with worn tyres and was not to return to traffic until 14 July. While at VF tyre-turning was done and attention given to traction motor sleeve bearings. Other work carried out included correction of earthing faults, battery modifications, new fan drives to one engine, boiler overhaul, new cab door locks, renewal of cab floors, compressor replacement, and repair of leaking pipework. On 24 September 1960 mileage stood at 427,472.

The locomotive ceased operation on BR following an engine failure in March 1961. It returned to VF where it was stored pending a decision on its future. It had covered over 450,000 miles on BR but further running was not necessary due to the delivery of the production Deltics.

In the autumn of 1961 a proposal was considered to modify the locomotive for trial operation in Canada where its power exceeded anything that indigenous manufacturers could then offer. The following modifications to comply with Canadian requirements were proposed:

1. Standard Canadian air brake system.
2. Automatic couplers and AAR drawgear.
3. New wheels of Monobloc type, 3ft 6in diameter.
4. Review of train-heating steam generator capacity.
5. The temperature control of the radiator fan and use of anti-freeze.
6. Conversion to right-hand drive.
7. Bogie overhaul due to high mileage.
8. Repairs to bodywork.
9. Headlamps and marker lights to Canadian standard.
10. Engine power adjustment to match radiator capacity, due to this being underestimated by $12\frac{1}{2}\%$ for heat dissipation.
11. Improved cab heating.
12. Fitting of cowcatchers.
13. Window demisters required.
14. Buffing load to meet 400 short tons standard.
15. Fuel tank fillers of Canadian standard.
16. Fitting of radio telephone.

Unfortunately, nothing came of this proposal.

The Deltic, the world's most powerful single-unit diesel locomotive, remained at VF until 1963, by which time some components had been removed, notably the engines, some of which found their way into the Class 55 engine pool. However, it was visually restored with some fake and unserviceable components for display at the Science Museum at South Kensington; it was taken by a new Class 37 locomotive to London, and thence by road to the museum on 28 April 1963, where it remains today.

Prototype *Deltic* passes under the original Harringay GN flyover with the 13.38 Doncaster-King's Cross on 27 March 1959. (*J. F. Aylard*)

Earning itself a secure foothold for the future (although Class 55 was already ordered). *Deltic* at Grantham while on the East Coast Main Line trials during 1959–61 leaves its characteristic smoke-screen as it starts its train. (*Brian Lee*)

The prototype *Deltic* sitting among 1875hp Co-Co diesels for Sudan in No 7 shop at Vulcan works on 16 March 1963, being prepared for preservation in the Science Museum, London, to which it was moved on 23 March 1963. (*GEC Traction Ltd*)

CHAPTER 2

CLASS 23 THE BABY DELTICS 1959–1963

The ten Type 'B' small Deltic locomotives were part of 40 main line diesel electrics ordered from English Electric (EE) under the pilot scheme for the acquisition of mainline diesel locomotives of the 1955 BR modernisation plan. EE received orders for ten 2000hp Type 'C' 1Co–Co1, ten 1100 hp Type 'B' Bo-Bo, and twenty 1000hp Type 'A' Bo-Bo locomotives.

The Baby Deltics of Type 'B' were EE contract CCF0875. The mechanical parts and erection of the locomotives was ordered from Vulcan Foundry (VF) Ltd, Newton-le-Willows on 23 January 1957, VF allocating its order numbers 6553/4 of 1957. The locomotives were built simultaneously in two batches of five.

As with all diesel locomotive contracts placed by BR, a list of required standard equipment and preferred fittings had to be included. These comprised the fitting of the Vapor-Clarkson type OK4616 train-heating steam generator of USA design, built under licence by J. Stone & Co Ltd, and capable of producing 1600lb of steam per hour; the overall locomotive height had to be not more than 12ft 8in, and provision was to be made by EE in the vacuum train pipe for fitting of trip-cock gear, both the latter requirements being due to the planned use of the Baby Deltics on the Metropolitan widened lines to Moorgate station, and on cross-London inter-regional freight workings.

Although it was originally intended that the traction motors used would be identical and interchangeable with the EE type 526 motor to be fitted on the Type 'A' 1000hp locomotives, during 1956 EE was given permission to modify the motor. English Electric wished to provide a higher low-speed continuous tractive effort of 30,000lb at 10mph as opposed to 25,000 lb at 12mph, thus losing standardisation.

The Baby Deltic was the only type 'B' design on order for BR to have nose-ends, all others having the flat-front cab, but it was not to penalise EE, nor was it detrimental to repeat orders, BR assured the company. Generally the locomotives' appearance was similar to the ten type 'C' EE locomotives and the later Type 3 1750hp EE locomotive for BR. All three were similar mechanically, in this respect being very conventional – a simple underframe with two inner 'I' beams and two outer channel sections crossed by welded members, and with end dragboxes. The superstructure was prefabricated, welded to the underframe and covered with welded steel panelling.

The bogies were generally similar to the Type 'A' locomotives, of fabricated type built up by welding and riveting. The side members were box sections with cross-members riveted to them. The bolster was carried on semi-elliptical springs supported by planks and inclined swing links, lateral movement of the bolster being limited by rubber blocks. Springing between the bogie frame and wheels was by nests of helical springs located between the frame and the equalising beam on each side, underslung from the axleboxes.

The engine was the 9-cylinder 18-piston Napier Deltic type T9–29 with exhaust-gas turbocharging and rated at 1100hp at 1600 rev/min, in addition to driving an EE type 835 main generator and EE 912 auxiliary generator.

The contract delivery dates for the locomotives were stated as follows:

D5900	12.7.58
D5901	30.9.58
D5902	15.10.58
D5903	31.10.58
D5904	15.11.58
D5905	30.11.58
D5906	15.12.58
D5907	31.12.58
D5908	15.1.59
D5909	31.1.59

A BR penalty clause of a half percent per week of delay was included, with a ceiling of 15 percent.

On 8 October BR changed the method of classification for its diesel locomotives from 'A' (800–1000 hp locomotives), 'B' (1100–1200 hp locomotives), and 'C' (2000 hp plus locomotives), to Types 1, 2 and 4 respectively, at the same time introducing a Type 3 covering the 1500–1700 hp range. The Baby Deltics became Type 2 and later Class 23 upon introduction of the computer-based classification and numbering system; Class 23 will be used in this work from this point.

The livery chosen for Class 23 under the direction of Mr E. G. M. Wilkes of Messrs Wilkes & Ashmore, the industrial design consultants responsible, was specified thus:

Locomotive body (upper) – Standard BR locomotive green.
Locomotive body (lower) – Light grey to BSS2660 5-058, applied as a broad band to bottom edge of body and around the nose end, where it changed colour to BSS2660 0-005 bright red.
Roof – Mid grey to BSS2660 9-100.
Bogies and undergear – Black.
Buffer casings and buffer beams –
BSS2660 0-005 bright red.
Numerals – White.
Crest – Small BR crest 14$\frac{3}{4}$in diameter.

Following reports of poor riding qualities by BR on the EE Type 1 locomotives, and that instrumentation had detected vertical oscillation at 53mph, which EE had not detected, resulted in BR questioning the use of the same bogie on Class 23. EE intended to fit shock absorbers between the equalising beams and the bogie frame, and as it turned out that the BR fears had been exaggerated, it was interesting to note that due to the need to reduce the weight of Class 23 the shock absorbers were not fitted upon delivery. They were, however, fitted later.

The weighing of the first locomotives at VF proved that the specified weight of 72 tons had been exceeded by three tons. This was unacceptable to BR so EE had to do some hard thinking on weight reduction. It was undesirable to scrap components, so where possible transfer to other BR work was done. The overweight of Class 23 was due partly to the mechanical parts being built up to weight for adhesion purposes and offset the light weight of the Deltic diesel engine, and heavier than specified auxiliary equipment. The brakes, fire fighting equipment, AWS equipment, flexible gangway connections, were all heavier, and the provision of radiators to cope with engine power of 1375hp added to the problem. The weight discrepancy is revealed by the following:

	Estimated weight (tons)	*Actual weight (tons)*
Equipment	26.0	27.8
Mechanical parts	42.2	43.9
Engine liquids	0.9	0.8
Consumable services	5.8	5.1

The train-heating steam generator (SG) should have weighed 2750lb according to Vapor-Clarkson in the USA, and EE had worked to this weight, but when the J. Stone British-built Stone-Vapor type OK4616 was delivered, complete with the required British standard fittings, it weighed 3448lb. EE feared that it would have to ask BR for a weight concession in water and fuel tank capacity. Joint EE/Stone discussions suggested that 260lb could be saved by redesign of SG fittings and mountings, plus the substitution of glass-reinforced plastic for the SG cabinet doors and side panels, instead of steel.

EE tried to persuade BR to accept a locomotive weighing 74.5 tons with only two-thirds water and fuel supplies, but J. F. Harrison refused, resulting in further heart-searching at EE as the locomotives were already behind delivery schedules.

To lighten the weight of the mechanical parts, the bogie frames and equalising beams had circular holes cut in them; oleo-pneumatic replaced standard steel buffers; buffer blocks changed from steel to aluminium as on the EE Class 83 electric locomotives; steel removable roof sections were replaced by alloy; lightweight fuel and water tanks instead of steel were included; aluminium radiator shutter; removal of inner sandboxes and replacing the remainder by aluminium instead of steel; and the omission with BR permission of flexible gangway connections. The Northey exhauster was replaced by a Reavell unit which was lighter in weight, taken from those ordered for use on Class 83. Many redundant items were used in Class 20 and Class 40.

When re-weighing of D5901 was planned at VF, very elaborate precautions were taken as listed below, the weighing being done on 2 March 1959:

1. Rails to be perfectly level. Any packing to be placed below locomotive axle centres to prevent rail deflection with locomotive in position.
2. Engine oil and cooling water systems two-thirds full.
3. Fuel oil tanks for engine and train-heating steam generator empty.
4. Water tank empty.
5. Northey exhauster, silencers, tailpipes, motors, base structure, and supporting frame for upper unit removed.
6. Compensating weights of 11cwt to replace

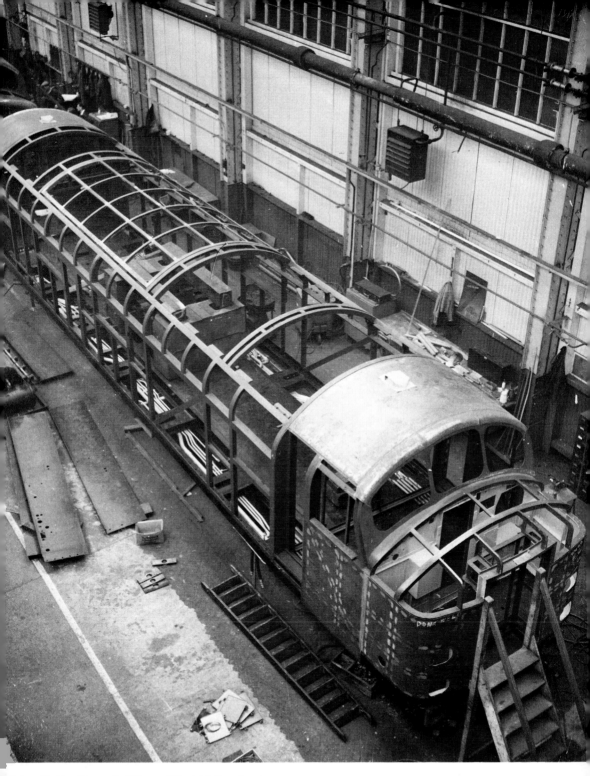

Baby Deltic Type 2 (Class 23) 1100hp Bo-Bo
superstructure being built at Vulcan Foundry during
1958. These mechanical parts were probably the
most robust provided for any BR diesel locomotive,
being built heavier to offset the much lighter diesel
engine being fitted. (*GEC Traction Ltd*)

Overhead view showing engine installation of a Baby Deltic at Vulcan Foundry in 1958.
Key: 1. Steam generator
2. Deltic T9–29 engine
3. EE main and auxiliary generator group
4. Control cubicle. (*GEC Traction Ltd*)

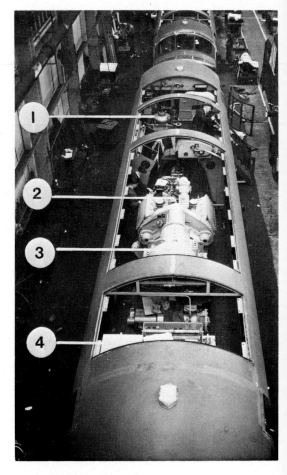

above to equal weight of Reavell unit, placed above and below cooker.
7. The outer reservoirs modified.
8. Batteries in position.
9. Four sandboxes two-thirds full – 60lb sand in each.
10. Buffers and blocks removed. Four 175lb weights in place, to simulate oleo buffers and blocks.
11. Boiler fuel tank empty and some items removed.
12. Wheels with $5\frac{1}{4}$in tyres.

On 10 March D5900 was similarly weighed but with the following variations.
5. Northey exhauster in position.
6. Not required.
7. Unmodified outer reservoirs. CO^2 bottles at No 2 end fitted.
9. Sandboxes empty.
11. Boiler fuel tank and fittings in place.
12. Wheels with $5\frac{1}{2}$in tyres.

Various other weighings with suitable alterations were made, and on 7 April D5909 was sent to BR Doncaster works for weighing the next day to compare the efficiency of VF and BR weighing equipment, the locomotive returning to VF on 9 April. The weighings were based on the following locomotive conditions, the weighings being:

Weighing No	Fuel Gal	Water Gal	Sand lb	Locomotive weights		
				Tons	Cwt	lb
1	270	250	240	72	6	1
2	230	300	240	72	6	2
3	250	250	240	72	4	1
4	350	450	240	73	8	2
5	450	500	240	73	17	0

From these results, apart from some argument about the accuracy of Doncaster's machine, BR decreed that a further 6cwt reduction was necessary. To achieve this EE put in hand the following modifications:
1. Remove remainder of redundant gangway items.

2. Cut holes in engine room floor under main generator and exhauster and cover with thinner gauge steel sheet.
3. Replace steel roof above control cubicle with aluminium.
4. Fit lighter reservoir mountings.
5. Replace three steel reservoirs with $\frac{1}{8}$in thick stainless steel ones.

The result was a weight reduction of 1165lb, and revised locomotive weight of 71tons 16cwt 12lb. Further weight reduction was not necessary, and after delivery of the locomotives the gangways and doors and panelling for the train-heating SG were refitted at Hornsey shed in mid-1959.

Before delivery, Class 23 ran test runs from VF to Chester, to Liverpool Edge Hill and on to Penrith via Preston. On these works trials BR drivers, inspectors, VF staff, EE and Napier engineers crowded into the locomotives as the lack of gangway connections prohibited access to the train while in motion.

D5902 was the first locomotive tested when on 1 April 1959 it worked with one carriage to Chester, doing its Penrith run on 3 April with nine coaches, during which it was stopped at Scout Green box on Shap on wet rails. On restarting the wheelslip system was allowed to function without moving the controller, and the train pulled away without difficulty.

The locomotives were delivered for acceptance to Doncaster works before entering service during April to June 1959. They were initially allocated to Hornsey shed until Finsbury Park depot was finished, although outstationed at Hitchin for use on outer suburban duties to King's Cross and Broad Street, and rarely via the Metropolitan widened lines to Moorgate where their exhaust fumes were not appreciated. They also took on Cambridge line workings, London area freights (although their intended use on cross-London freights never materialised) and on King's Cross empty stock duties.

The Deltic T9–29 engines were delayed due to a late decision to supercharge, and although rated at

General arrangement of Class 23. (*GEC Traction Ltd*)

1100hp the main generator was designed for development to 1250hp. The engines proved very satisfactory in service initially and their small size left plenty of space for maintenance, making them popular with depot staff. Early problems included leaking high-pressure fuel pipes, which defect was rectified by tightening joints or renewal of pipes; broken lubricating oil pressure pump quillshafts; low water level in header tanks causing engine shutdowns due to the coolant being forced by high pressure leakage back into the header tank and out of the overflow, thus preventing the low water level switch from operating. This fault did not prevent restarting of engines because after shut-down the coolant drained back into the engine.

The discovery of poorly-seated injector adaptors, and of doubtful fit and seals on the cylinder liner locating adaptor plugs revealed on affected engines a few liners with fine cracks radiating from the holes into which the liner locating adaptor plug was screwed, necessitating engine changes. By mid-August 1959 the engines were reported to be running well and seven engines had had injector adaptor modifications by the end of the month. By early October five engines had

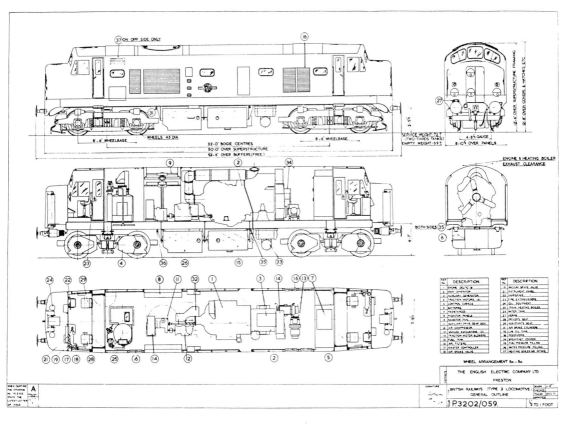

been changed because of fractured cylinder liners. The following month the failure of three turbo-charger turbine bearings – making four cases since entering service – at a similar number of service hours, enabled preventive action as others approached those hours. By this time seven locomotives had had their engines changed, and EE was being assailed by reports that competitive Type 2 locomotives on the ER were achieving 30–40,000 miles per casualty. The failure of Class 23 auxiliary equipment – largely proprietary components supplied by specialist subcontractors – proved a serious problem by the end of 1959. Failures due to equipment being inadequate for its task took place so frequently that spares were soon exhausted.

Early troubles with the clutch plate and the drive shaft between the auxiliary gearbox and the air compressor were initially dealt with by using spare clutch plates, and failure of the rubber/metal flexible coupling of the shaft by fitting temporary solid shafts. The solid shafts had neither clutch nor coupling, but brass bolts designed for easy shearing were fitted in the flange mounting to the auxiliary gearbox to protect this and the engine in case of air compressor failure. The drive shaft had its flexible coupling removed and steel rings welded in to provide a solid shaft until a new flexible shaft was available. By August 1959 D5900–8 had averaged 9000 miles each, and D5909 3000 miles, and by the end of September all the flexible couplings but one had failed. The locomotives had to be kept in service, so weaker clutch springs to permit the clutch to slip at high torque were used to lengthen clutch life at the expense of clutch linings, and ease the acute spares situation.

In January 1960 a new Rotoflex-Metalastik coupling of larger size fitted with a centring device was adopted. This had a bearing around the coupling to the clutch shaft supported from the clutch housing. This unit was simpler with sufficient axial flexibility to eliminate the troubles with the splined hub in the clutch plate. Fitting was completed by May 1960.

The provision of auxiliary drive by a power take-off shaft from the free end of the Deltic engine proved troublesome and expensive. The power was transmitted from the engine to the auxiliary gearbox supplying horizontal drives to the air compressor, one traction motor blower, and by vertical drive to the roof mounted radiator fan. Soon after delivery of the locomotives EE engineers noted that at engine idling speed the gear

trains in the gearbox were very noisy and that considerable backlash was evident due to the combined action of the machines involved.

The auxiliary gearbox itself required constant attention and frequent replacement to keep the locomotives running, the situation being aggravated by the inadequacies of the driving and driven shafts coupled to it, and maintenance costs would remain high until these were resolved. Between December 1959 and April 1960 the locomotives received new compressor drive shafts, flexible drives and traction motor blower shafts, but failures continued.

Failure of the cardan shaft from the engine to the auxiliary gearbox began in November 1959, setting the stage for a spate of such failures, rising to serious proportions by 1961. Failure of the shaft often resulted in severe engine damage when the flailing shaft smashed the adjacent engine coolant pipe, interrupting the flow of coolant and resulting in severe engine overheating and multiple piston seizures. EE suspected shaft metal fatigue but the shaft manufacturers said the shaft had bowed due to being fouled by a crossmember, causing kinking and fracture; as the nearest item was the shaft guard $\frac{7}{8}$in from the shaft EE thought that fouling had taken place after fracture. The shaft had run for over 7000 hours and EE said that all shafts needed to be reconditioned.

Between November 1961 and May 1962 six Deltic engine failures involved five shaft failures, and in four cases the coolant pipe was broken. Napier said that the locomotives should be taken out of service until the cardan shaft was redesigned and replaced. Opinions continued to differ on the cause of the failures until by 1963 the toll on the Deltic engines and loss of service with the locomotives had become intolerable, failures in some cases being at very low engine service hours. Tests on cardan shafts revealed their tendency to whirl at about two-thirds of the Deltic engine maximum rpm rating.

Other persistent problems were leaking, overheating and variable pressures in the oil and water cooling radiators from 1959 to 1961. Faulty soldering, deterioration of gaskets, or bolted joints, caused the leaking, all being cured in varying degrees. Overheating was due to blocked radiators, incorrectly set thermostats, poor external/internal radiator cleaning. The radiator manufacturers blamed the leakages on differential expansion, and vibration from the locomotives' superstructure, which was transmitted by too-rigid

Above: D5908 in the yard at Hornsey locomotive depot in 1959. (*GEC Traction Ltd*)

Below: Line up of eight stored Class 23 awaiting refurbishing at Stratford in 1963, D5909 nearest the camera. (*David Sharp*)

pipe connections and hoses, convoluted hoses being fitted together with rubber mountings in the radiator frame to combat this. Troubles with the radiator cooling fan drive caused BR to consider rebuilding the locomotives in mid-1961 unless reliability and freedom from the resultant overheating of engine coolant was overcome.

By October 1960 the locomotives had run individual mileages of only 40–60000 miles, due largely to equipment failures, and since the first locomotives entered service in April 1959 forty-four engine changes had been made on the ten locomotives at Stratford works, a number having had five engine changes each. Some of the causes were:

1 Fractured cylinder liners	10
2 Turbo-charger turbine failure	7
3 Engine modifications	7
4 Life expired turbo-charger turbine	3
5. Engine dephased	1
6. Piston failure	5
7. Miscellaneous faults	4

By October 1960 four main areas of Deltic engine problems were outlined by Napier:

1. The fracture of cylinder liners, resulting from stresses set up during assembly of the engines. The tightening of the crankcase bolts caused the cylinder block to bear hard against the injector adaptor, itself screwed into the cylinder liner. The area of local stress thus set up in the liner led to fractures.

2. Turbo-charger turbine bearing failures caused by back pressure in the locomotive exhaust system. The exhaust gases were leaking past the turbine oil labyrinth seals and forming carbon deposits on the turbine rotor causing a heavy end thrust on the bearings which they were not designed to withstand. Seals, air delivery, and routing were modified.

3. Fractured liners due to erosion (brought about by electrolitic action) in the threaded injector adaptor hole machining. Recuttering of injector adaptor holes was done at Finsbury Park, and plating of the holes with lead, tin, gold etc.

4. Seizure of pistons due to the chemical erosion of the underside of the piston crown due to the heat transfer from the crown and the alignment of the piston being adversely affected by any unevenness in the surface of either the underside of the piston crown or the top of the gudgeon pin

housing, which were in contact with each other. Certain of the engine lubricants were found to promote surface erosion and thereby an uneven surface, hence the heat transfer problem, slight surface machining defects contributing to this.

Engine cooling deficiencies resulted in a temporary but slight derating of the Deltic engines to 1025hp until at the recommendation of EE redesigned and modified air-ducting could be fitted to the locomotives to reduce the operating temperatures of the engines. Concurrently the opinions as to the amount of cooling air required to meet the cooling rate of the locomotive radiators led to the decision in late 1960 to fit 12-bladed instead of 8-bladed cooling fans to give sufficient margin to meet all contingencies.

In July 1960 the intention was to modify the Deltic engines with the aim of obtaining an operating period of 4000 hours between engine changing. The Napier plans to introduce a programme to completely rebuild the Deltic engines, incorporating all necessary modifications, was accepted by BR and the first rebuilt ones were due for delivery in December 1960. The modifications included fully modified cylinder liners, new pistons in cases where incorrect lubricating oils had damaged the pistons, modification of the top crankcases with stiffer webs, provision of increased bearing area for the turbo-charger compressor impeller bearings and change of material from aluminium to steel, fitting of new seals on the coolant pump and provision of increased clearances in the thermostatic valves, modifying the engine governor with spring links on the control linkage.

On 8 October 1960 four out of the ten locomotives were reported to be out of service due to repairs, in spite of there being 16 Deltic engines available, 11 belonging to BR and five to Napier – sixty per cent more engines than locomotives!

The continuing problems with the locomotives resulted in a BR suggestion of July 1961 that the Deltic engines be replaced by the EE 8SVT 8-cylinder Vee-type engine. EE pointed out that this would add eight tons to the locomotive weight, and that most of the locomotives' loss of availability was due to the time spent in works for engine changes; that in fact when running, the locomotives were the best in availability and had the lowest maintenance costs of any BR locomotive – over the previous two weeks the availability had been 93·9 percent.

Difficulties continued, and in May 1962 another

Above: D5904 passes Vulcan Foundry en route to Doncaster works on delivery to the Eastern Region in April 1959. (*GEC Traction Ltd*)

Below: D5903 passing through Finsbury Park station in 1959. (*GEC Traction Ltd*)

View of a pair of Class 23 bogies after weight reduction modifications — note circular holes in bogie headstocks. (*GEC Traction Ltd*)

failures, the existing design of piston was troublesome owing to loosening of the hydural piston crowns. Modified fits and increased tightening were not completely successful in eliminating the problem. The proposed cure was by the adoption of a piston with modified crown and skirt, with increased flexibility to eliminate loosening.

The main bearings and housings showed signs of fretting in the main bearing caps where clamped into the crankcase. This was not serious, but stiffer cross bolts were introduced to remove the problem. The main bearings were in perfect condition.

On 1 October 1962 the individual locomotive mileages stood at:

D5900	148460
D5901	146620
D5902	109040
D5903	113650
D5904	128360
D5905	133210
D5906	145810
D5907	159500
D5908	141580
D5909	106350

EE report was published which again dealt with the Deltic engine and its problems. By this time all the failures had been investigated and it was stated that with further modification the engine should be reliable, even though it was less robust than conventional rail traction diesel engines in service. A survey of 24 engine failures revealed that 13 were due to fractured cylinder liners, two to defective liner sealing rings, one each for output bearings and auxiliary generator drive, five due to external causes such as freezing up etc, and two cases still under investigation. The most serious of these was due to the cylinder liners fracturing; these were typical fatigue cracks from the outer edge of the injector adaptor holes and ran through to the bore and inlet ports. The cause was erosion pitting at the adaptor hole seatings. Efforts to prevent erosion had failed and a much thicker and improved liner was designed, incorporating better securing and cooling. Cavitation erosion of the cylinder block due to untreated coolant water being used with the light alloy blocks was occurring in the coolant space adjacent to the cylinder liner scrolls (specially-treated coolant water was essential with Deltic engines).

Although not responsible for any engine

Electrical problems were not a great problem on Class 23. The main generators did give trouble during the second half of 1959 because of blackening of alternate bars and burning of groups of bars on their commutators, causing in addition rapid brush wear. Cleaning and re-grinding of the commutators, plus trials with other types of brushes, were undertaken. Some trouble with main generator armature bearings necessitated their redesign.

Due to the main generator armatures becoming out of balance it was necessary for EE to rebalance these during overhaul of the power units after removal from the locomotives. It was opined that the 'out-of-balance' trouble was due to the problems with the engine overspeed governors which, although designed to trip at 1680–1700 rev/min, were failing to do so. EE having tested the main generators when new to 2000 rev/min, it was found that the armatures had gone out of balance due to the movement of the varnish in the end windings, which in turn was caused by excessive engine overspeeding. The defect made it necessary to replace the spherically-mounted output shaft bearing on the engines returned to Napier. Traction motor troubles were few and flashovers were very rare.

CHAPTER 3

CLASS 23 REFURBISHMENT AND NEW ENGINES, 1963–1971

The oft wished-for re-engining theme to convert Class 23 into more conventional machines by fitting a traditional EE Vee-type diesel engine, standard with that fitted to the English Electric Type 1 (Class 20) resurrected itself in early 1962. During February 1962 EE estimates for re-engining Class 23 surfaced – a very different scheme, which would convert the locomotives into a Type 3 Bo-Bo of 1650hp and 76 tons weight by fitting them with a Deltic 18-cylinder engine, as in the EE Type 5 3300hp Co-Co locomotives which had recently been delivered to BR. English Electric was greatly in favour of such a re-engining, using the complete 1650hp Deltic engine, generator, auxiliary generator, and control system standard to the 3300hp locomotives, and certainly tried to lead BR along this path, disregarding other schemes. In June 1962 the EE 8-cylinder Vee-type engine schemes appeared, one using the 8 SVT and offering either steam heating or electric train heating (eth), plus a similar proposal using the uprated 8 CSVT II engine and either of the alternative heating schemes.

July 1962 saw work well advanced on a new revolutionary EE diesel engine type known as the 'U' series engine. A prototype engine fitted with an EE type 835 main generator and EE type 913 auxiliary generator was on the test bed at the EE diesel engine test plant at Brownsover Hall, Rugby; it was desirable to gain traction experience for the engine, making the Class 23 locomotive an obvious candidate. Suggestions that BR be asked to make available either 10000/1, the LMS pioneer Co-Co locomotives, or one of the new EE Type 3 Co-Co locomotives of BR for testing the engine were discounted because of the size and weight of their mechanical parts. With a Class 23 it was possible to create an 80-ton 90mph 20-ton axle load locomotive with a maximum starting tractive effort of 45000 lb at 25% adhesion.

English Electric calculated that such a locomotive with the 'U' type engine set at 1800hp would be able to take a 750-ton express freight from Crewe to Glasgow in $365\frac{1}{2}$ minutes without exceeding 55mph, or on the same route a 10-coach passenger train of 350 tons in $247\frac{1}{2}$ minutes at a maximum speed of 90mph. The 'U' series engine was intended to provide EE with a robust lightweight rail traction diesel engine to supplement the RK/V heavyweight engine ranges and the Deltic opposed-piston engines.

BR was agreeable to the scheme to traction-test a 'U' type engine, but the selection of the Class 23 was dependent on BR requirements regarding re-engining the locomotives. EE went ahead, planning the scheme based on Class 23 and preparing drawings for the modifications required and the auxiliaries needing replacement.

In February 1963 it was decided by EE that initially the engine be fitted at 1550hp, it being of the type 12 CSUT, and BR agreed to one locomotive being released to EE, stating that EE could choose from among the Class 23 locomotives stored at Stratford. D5901 was chosen. The engine to be fitted would be one of two metricated engines then being built at the EE Preston works and the first was promised for delivery to VF in July 1963.

D5901 was taken quietly into Vulcan Foundry on 6 March 1963. The locomotive was in poor condition, with many parts missing or damaged, so that EE was reluctant to pay for these and considered that BR should cover the cost of the rectification work not directly attributable to the new engine project. Considerable work was necessary to bring D5901 up to the standard required for it to be re-engined, a goodly number of items of equipment had to be removed, resited, or replaced by different or improved equipment, and some modifications to the mechanical parts – underframe, superstructure, and bogies – put in hand. At the same time full updating of the control gear and the fitting of improved sound-proofing were carried out.

The underframe had to have the engine-well enlarged to take six engine mountings (the Deltic engine previously requiring only four) and additionally the relocation of mountings and the equipment for the air compressor, exhausters, No 2 traction motor blower, No 1 traction motor blower, auxiliary gearbox, lubricating oil priming pump, radiators, pipe runs etc.

The superstructure required some new roof sections, new air intakes at cantrail level, additional air-filter louvred openings at No 2 end, while in the radiator compartment a complete revision was necessary. Cabling, interior lighting, fire detection/extinguishing equipment had also to be altered.

So far as the bogies were concerned the EE type 533 traction motors were retained but re-geared to a ratio of 58:17 and new primary and secondary springing, compensating beams and axleboxes fitted to suit the 20-ton axle loading of the re-engined locomotive. All this work was covered by EE contract CCR 1500, the locomotive to be ready for traffic by 30 September 1963.

The 'U' type engine was designed specifically for rail traction to provide a high-speed diesel engine of compact dimensions and moderate weight, and to have a high degree of reliability and durability. The power/weight ratio was a marked improvement over the current EE RK/V range and the engine was designed to be developed to higher ratings. The leading particulars of the 'U'

type engine are summarised in this table:

Vee-form angle	45°
Cylinder bore/stroke	$7\frac{11}{16}$in × $8\frac{1}{2}$in (195mm × 216mm)
Continuous traction rating to BSS 2953:1958	1550bhp at 1500rpm
Normal speed range	600/1500rpm
Bmep at traction rating	173lb/sq in (11.96kg/sq cm)
Piston speed at 1500rpm	2125ft/min (10.8m/sec)
Weight of engine	17,400lb (7,900kg)
Weight per bhp	11.2lb/hp (5.1kg/hp)
Number of cylinders	12

During May 1963 EE had established suitable duties for the locomotive which was then being called DP3 due to the desire of BR that the locomotive's numbering should not be confused with its own locomotive fleet, bearing in mind the initial rating of the 12 CSUT engine of 1550hp and its axle loading of $19\frac{3}{4}$ tons. Such an axle load meant that the locomotive would have to be restricted to certain routes, assuming that the locomotive would return to the Eastern Region (ER) after conversion. It was less powerful than the EE Type 3/Class 37, but was a useful competitor to the uprated Brush-built Type 2 A1A A1A locomotives of 104 tons weight and 1600hp on the ER. It was felt that the Liverpool Street – King's Lynn service would suit the locomotive admirably:

DIRECT COMPARISON BETWEEN THE EXISTING LOCOMOTIVE AND RE-ENGINED LOCOMOTIVE (TWO VERSIONS)

Detail	Existing 1100hp locomotive	Proposed 1550hp locomotive	Uprated locomotive 1800hp
Weight in working order	73t 17cwt	79t 0cwt	79t 0cwt
Length over buffers	52ft 6in	52ft 6in	52ft 6in
Engine	Deltic T9–29	EE 12 CSUT	EE 12 CSUAT
Rating (traction)	1100hp at 1600rpm	1550hp at 1500rpm	1800hp at 1500rpm
Maximum speed	75mph	90mph	90mph
Maximum tractive effort	46,200lb	45,000lb	45,000lb
Continuous rated tractive effort	31,800lb	26,200lb	26,200lb
Speed at continuous rating	9mph	16.9mph	19.8mph
Gear ratio	63:17	58:19	58:19
Wheel diameter	3ft 7in	3ft 7in	3ft 7in

Service	Load (tons)	All-out time inc. stops (min)	Timetable (min)	Make-up (%)
Liverpool St–King's Lynn	292/313	121.5	138	12
Liverpool St–Norwich (non-stop)	292/313	118.3	120	1.4
Liverpool St–Norwich (stopping)	292/313	139.7	145	3.6
King's Cross–Sheffield (Pullman)	240/251	156.7	165	5.0

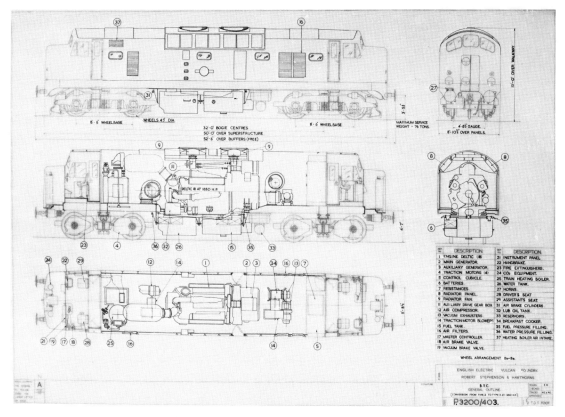

General arrangement of the preferred English Electric re-engine proposal for fitting a single 18-cylinder D18–25 Deltic engine to produce a 1650hp 76-ton Type 3 locomotive. (*GEC Traction Ltd*)

For freight work it was predicted that 900-ton loads on grades of 1 in 100, or 750 tons on 1 in 70, could be hauled easily.

Work on the 'U' type engine ran into difficulties during May 1963 and its delivery was put back to early August, subsequently slipping further, with the result that by early October 1963 D5901 was completely ready to receive the engine but was locked-up at Newton-le-Willows because no further work was possible until receipt of the engine. With the engine reassembled by early November, delivery was considered possible at the end of the month, the engine having completed its 1000 hours endurance trials at load/speed factors of 73% and 82% respectively. Stripping-down revealed few faults of consequence.

Internal changes at the EE Diesel Engine and Traction divisions during December 1963 resulted in the whole of the 'U' engine project being terminated by EE, leaving D5901 minus engine at Vulcan Foundry. On 6 December the order was

issued to convert D5901 back to its original form as a Deltic-powered Class 23. Fortunately, concurrent work was already under way at VF on a thorough refurbishing programme for the remaining nine examples of Class 23, D5900 and D5902-9, which had been taken there engineless during July/August 1963, so D5901 was tacked on to this contract.

All the redundant equipment from D5901, together with the 12 CSUT engines were stored by EE, a very unsatisfactory outcome, for if the project had been pursued to fruition it could possibly have resulted in a better rail traction engine than the Paxman units currently favoured for the High-Speed Trains (HST) of BR.

D5901 was converted, so far as was practical, back to an orthodox Class 23 – a costly process – but it was to retain modified engine-well, compressor mountings, cooker, additional walkway cover plates, revised 'B' side radiator shutter operating gear, fire detection equipment, and interior lighting arrangement.

The refurbishing of Class 23 was the subject of an EE quotation of 4 September 1962, based on and making allowance for the general condition of the locomotives, and the work had to put them into first-class order for reliable service running. During consideration of the work it was decided to re-design the engine-to-auxiliary gearbox drive and the drive to the air compressor and cooling fan, but plans to employ other than the Deltic T9-29 engine did not proceed. Sound insulation (a long standing source of irritation to BR) was to be brought up to standard. Even though in 1961–2 EE had supplied BR with additional materials for this for fitting to the locomotives at Stratford, not all locomotives had been equally treated. EE wished to refurbish and modify the first locomotive at VF so that all the work undertaken could be easily controlled and thoroughly tested. BR was thinking of doing the remainder itself, but in June 1963 EE was trying to obtain the work for VF and great effort, which eventually succeeded, was put in to persuade BR to contract the work.

Refurbishing was very thorough, the schedule involving the removal of all equipment and fittings, cleaning, repainting internally and externally, removal of fuel and water tanks, brake gear, bogies, radiators, air filters, auxiliary equipment such as traction motor blowers, exhausters, fuel pump, brake equipment, control equipment, train-heating steam generator, auxiliary drive gearbox, the overhaul and testing of all equipment which was returned to its respective maker, or to the appropriate EE group works. The re-installation of all this, plus thorough testing, was specified under contract CCR 1351.

The livery chosen for the refurbished loco-motives was to conform with that of the Type 5 3300hp Deltic locomotives, ie two-tone green with a nose-front yellow warning panel. They were to retain this livery until withdrawal, except for D5909 which was painted rail blue at Doncaster works in 1968.

As the work progressed various changes in the contract were made, such as the fitting of nose-front route indicators, and involving the removal of the gangway doors in the nose and plating-over the apertures, modifications to the driver's desk, seats, new fillers for the SG water tanks, frost protection and other alterations. Napier overhauled and rebuilt the Deltic engines to comply with the firm's latest standards, the first engine arriving at VF in March 1964 for 200–250 hours testing in D5908 which was third in the refurbishing programme.

In order to avoid recurrence of the problems of 1959–63, redesign of the cardan shaft from the

engine to the auxiliary gearbox was undertaken. The new shafts were resilient units for in-line mounting, while the previous shafts could not because of their design be mounted in-line without severely damaging them. As it turned out, the locomotives were returned to service with an interim type of shaft known as the 2-4 shaft which in fact proved quite satisfactory in service, but were replaced by the intended 6-6 shaft of even more substantial design as these became available at Finsbury Park depot in early 1965. The 6-6 shaft was 17% larger in diameter and some 35% thicker in section than the locomotive's original shaft, and it was dynamically balanced twice, first on the tube assembly and then on the whole shaft assembly, complete with rubber bushes and end couplings. All parts were numbered and stamped to avoid incorrect assembly. Shaft vibrations due to secondary whirl, which caused the fatigue and failure of the original shafts, and which can occur on shafts within the engine running range, were eliminated as the critical whirl of the new shaft was above the maximum overspeed of the Deltic engine.

Future failure of the Deltic engine, radiator, or water system, or of a cardan shaft driving auxiliaries would not in future lead to multiple piston seizures, because a flow protection system similar to that on the Type 5 Deltics was fitted to the refurbished Class 23. This shut down the engine when coolant flow was interrupted. Additional shaft guards were provided to protect adjacent coolant pipes.

To reduce the loading on the auxiliary gearbox, an electrically-driven Westinghouse air compressor of type 2EC388 was fitted, rendering the mechanically-driven Westinghouse 2EC72A unit surplus, there being no similar units on BR. In June 1964 the delivery period for the refurbished locomotives was given as 19 June to 27 November 1964, this being adhered to.

The cooling radiators for coolant and lubricating oil were cleaned and overhauled and epoxy resin dip-coated by EE prior to refitting, in the hope of obviating any repetition of the problems of previous years.

Before the refurbished locomotives began to return to service, a maintenance contract covering only the Deltic engines was drawn up, based on a rate per engine hour, the rate decreasing as the contract engine hours increased on two-yearly cycles. It was proposed that repair periodicity would be initially 4000 hours, and then 6000

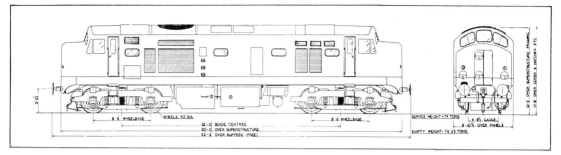

Side elevation showing external modifications proposed in 1963 for the conversion of D5901 to take the EE 12 CSUT 1500hp Vee engine. (*Brian Webb*)

hours, and finally 8000 hours up to mid-1968. The first engine repairs would start in mid-1966 and not more than two locomotives were to be out of service awaiting engines at any one time, regardless of whether this was due to regular overhaul requirements or through premature failure.

As the locomotives were returned to BR they were accepted at Doncaster works, working their trials with 250- to 290-ton trains of coaching stock to Grantham and Peterborough and with freight stock of up to 750 tons to Whitemoor. The locomotives were delivered to Doncaster starting with D5904 on 25 June 1964 and finishing with D5901 – the erstwhile 'U' engine locomotive – on 14 April 1965, the locomotives arriving at Finsbury Park depot as follows:

D5900	2.10.64
D5901	29.4.65
D5902	27.11.64
D5903	4.9.64
D5904	1.7.64
D5905	20.12.64
D5906	29.10.64
D5907	31.3.65
D5908	18.8.64
D5909	16.7.64

Problems began almost immediately when flexible hose in the engine lubricating oil system began to come adrift, causing oil spillages and provoking engine failures, and leaking oil cooling radiator matrices. The former was dealt with by improving the fixing clips on the hose and by staying the hitherto unsupported hoses to stop them swaying (which had been pulling off the hose) and the latter was put down to radiator corrosion, although clipping of the hoses caused the oil radiator matrices to leak also. The fact that BR itself had taken out the Deltic engines at Stratford

prior to refurbishing, and that pipework etc was dumped in the engine rooms of the locomotives, in some cases with various fittings missing, including hose clips, meant that some locomotives were probably turned out from VF without clips fitted.

During March 1965 a joint EE/BR report on the hose problem drew the following conclusions:

1. All failures followed extremely cold nights when the locomotives had been standing overnight at Hitchin.
2. Failures took place approximately 30 minutes after starting the engines.
3. New type hose clips were fitted in January 1965.
4. There were three cases of hoses near the oil thermostat coming off the pipe connection, twice due to loose clips.
5. EE bench tests had proved that the hoses and clips could withstand pressures far higher than found in the locomotives in service.
6. EE suggested better grip for the hoses on the pipe connections.

Radiator leakage continued and BR was by this time becoming impatient, especially in view of the expense of overhauling the radiators at refurbishing, and the likelihood of having to fit new radiators regardless of this. Radiators were continually passing to and from the makers' works, or to EE for inspection, testing or repairs throughout 1965–6.

The persistent radiator problems indicated that the time and money spent on them had been largely unsuccessful and it was usual for the locomotives to be in service with leaking radiators! EE had pointed out to BR during refurbishing that during cleaning they were found to exhibit serious chemical attack, due in part to bi-metal corrosion and the use by BR of unsuitable treatments in the coolant water. As a result, six sets of radiators

The conversion of D5901 to take the 'U' engine and produce prototype locomotive DP3 was terminated after much work had been undertaken on the locomotive. Here D5901 is seen at Vulcan works in 1964 being re-converted to a standard refurbished Class 23. (*Brian Webb collection*)

were retubed in brass and four sets dipped in epoxy resin as a temporary measure.

In early 1966 a new trouble manifested itself, due either to failure of soldered joints around the radiator tubes in the header plate, or fracture of the tubes adjacent to the header plate. It was agreed in March 1966 by BR and the radiator manufacturers that the cause was differential expansion between the brass tubes and the radiator steel frame, and that in spite of slip joints in the frame to cater for this contingency they were not functioning properly. It was decided to fit brass sides instead of steel to the matrix and improve the design of the slip joints. Between May and August 1967 ten locomotive sets of radiators were put through the makers' works and fitted to the locomotives.

At the suggestion of English Electric, BR decided to purchase two sets of an alternative

make of radiator for use in Class 23. These radiators had copper tubes with cooling fins and were designed with all the previous radiator problems in mind, being almost completely interchangeable with them in fitting and connections; they were kept as spare sets.

On 6 January 1967 the following individual mileages for Class 23 locomotives since refurbishing were quoted:

D5900	107,970
D5901	88,160
D5902	102,950
D5903	116,340
D5904	124,070
D5905	104,510
D5906	101,930
D5907	89,330
D5908	111,600
D5909	125,510

As the first stage of BR's intention to take over the complete overhaul of the Deltic engines used in both Class 23 and Class 55, it negotiated with Napier an agreed training scheme for the BR Doncaster works staff who would be concerned with the Deltic engine work. It was to take place at Napier's Liverpool works. The training scheme was set up and run so that BR could take on the Deltic T9-29 engine overhaul by April 1968 and phase-in the work. A lot of expense, time, and effort had gone into this scheme, when it was decreed that Class 23 would be withdrawn from service prematurely as part of the National Traction Plan policy to eliminate the numerically small and non-standard locomotive classes. The decision dashed the planned programme for Deltic engine repair at Doncaster, in spite of the steps taken to implement this. It had been intended that the work and experience gained on the smaller T9-29 engine would pave the way for the second stage scheduled for 1969 when the larger Deltic D18-25 engines from Class 55 locomotives would start to be Doncaster-maintained.

English Electric had large stocks of spares for the T9-29 engines, as following the extensive refurbishing of Class 23, the company had assumed a full life for the locomotives and their engines. BR had intimated that it would ultimately purchase the spares, but there was no written agreement on this. Napier had provided staff, spares lists, tools, jigs fixtures etc, to enable Doncaster to take-over engine work at a cost of some £9,000, and had a commitment to the work said to be in the region of £150,000. Much

Refurbished D5907 with an empty stock train at Hitchin on 8 February 1967. (*H. L. Holland*)

negotiation to resolve this ensued. In June 1968 BR informed EE that they would not require any more T9-29 engines for Class 23, apart from two then under repair at Napier's on 2 May 1968.

The Class 23 locomotives were certainly much improved by the refurbishing work, and apart from the radiator problems were now reliable locomotives. Availability for the refurbished locomotives was regularly 80–90%, and 100% in some periods. Withdrawal from service under the National Traction Plan was spread between September 1968 and March 1971.

The locomotives again congregated at Stratford prior to being sold for scrap and were used to supply spares for the locomotives still at work. In fact the final two, D5905 and D5909, remained at Stratford until mid-1973, being used as a source of spares for D5901, which gained a new lease of life

by being transferred to the Railway Technical Centre at Derby during August 1969 for use on various test trains such as the tribometer train, a mobile laboratory unit for surveying rail-wheel adhesion. It remained in use until late 1975 when it was again withdrawn, arriving at Doncaster works on 18 February 1976, and remaining there with some equipment removed until February/March 1977 when it was cut-up for scrap. Its Deltic engine was acquired by GEC Traction Ltd which as successor to EE had a claim on the engine in order to replace engines lent to BR to assist in the spares provision, the other engine having already been acquired. The dismantling of the T9-29 engines to enable the re-use of the few suitable components in the D18-25 Class 55 engines was undertaken at the Paxman works of GEC Diesels Ltd, Colchester.

A ballast train near Hadley Wood with D5903 and D5905 in multiple-unit, 8 October 1967. (*D. A. Idle*)

Above: D5909 and D5905 were withdrawn in March 1971 and February 1971 respectively. Here they lie at Stratford on 8 August 1971 awaiting disposal for scrap. D5909 was the only Class 23 locomotive to receive the BR rail blue livery. (*Roland Hummerston*)

Below: D5901, withdrawn in December 1968 and transferred to the Railway Technical Centre at Derby for hauling test trains, is seen passing Coseley on 19 February 1973 with the tribometer train on the Birmingham–Wolverhampton line. (*G. F. Bannister*)

CHAPTER 4

CLASS 55 DELTIC DESIGN AND DEVELOPMENT

From the start English Electric assumed that the BR 3300hp Deltic locomotives would be identical to the prototype apart from loading gauge, which EE thought would be easily accommodated, so all EE thinking was based on the prototype. Discussions on 30 September 1957 between the EE Chairman, Lord Nelson of Stafford, and the British Transport Commission on the possible use of such locomotives on the East Coast Main Line brought out the requirement that the new locomotives would have to comply with the locomotive loading gauge (L1) and coaching stock loading gauge (C1), and also have a wide route availability. These were important, since the locomotives were to be used on other BR routes following planned electrification of the East Coast Main Line at that time.

English Electric examined the prototype *Deltic* to ascertain modifications to suit BR and to prepare costings, from which it was hoped to prepare estimates for a batch of 23–24 locomotives for BR. EE had decided that the BR locomotives would be as near as possible to the prototype and intended actually to sell the prototype to BR as part of the contract after suitable modifications.

Running experience with the prototype dictated some modifications to suit BR and in October 1957 these were:

Category A – Modifications to suit BR requirements

A1. Locomotive to be of L1/C1 loading gauge – prototype was L2.
A2. AWS to be provided.
A3. Dead man equipment required.
A4. Two exhausters, not one as fitted to prototype. Brake valve moved from right- to left-hand side of driver.
A5. To be able to negotiate $4\frac{1}{2}$-chain curves – prototype was 6 chains.
A6. 2500lb/hr capacity steam generator for train heating.
A7. Buffer standout to be 1ft 3in., not $10\frac{1}{2}$in.
A8. Fuel capacity increased to 820 gallons.

A9. Toilet to be fitted, complete with wash basin, hot and cold water.
A10. Breakfast cooker and hotplates required.
A11. Redesign of dragbox to take automatic or buckeye couplers.
A12. Steel-tyred wheels required, not solid steel disc.
A13. BR standard brake blocks.
A14. Marker lights, headcode discs, route indicators required.
A15. Improved cab heating to 4kW minimum.
A16. Restyling of locomotive.
A17. Compliance with BR fire regulations and fitting CO_2 equipment.
A18. Fitting water-softening equipment in water tanks.
A19. BTC breakdown/lifting equipment to be fitted.
A20. Snowplough attachments on bogie frames.

Category B – Modifications required as a result of service experience or to facilitate maintenance/manufacture

B.1. Improved radiator capacity to suit maximum engine temperature.
B2. Repositioning of thermostats.
B3. Reconsideration and redesign of engine pipework.
B4. Underframe-mounted lubricating oil tank, possibly surplus to requirements.
B5. Improvement of inner sanders.
B6. Solid equalising beams, not fluted.
B7. Solid instead of hollow axles.
B8. Smith-Stone speedometer, not Elliot.
B9. Redesign of instrument panel.
B10. Redesign of axlebox covers.
B11. Illumination required on assistant's panel.
B12. No nose-end headlight.
B13. Replacement of light alloy construction by steel in some areas.
B14. Improvement of traction motor lead cleats.

Compliance with the L1/C1 gauge restrictions brought possible axle load restrictions, but as BR gave no weight concessions EE intended to retain light-alloy construction and hollow axles to avoid the penalty of the BR P/D ratio (pounds weight wheel diameter) which would make necessary 45in instead of 43in wheels.

The prototype *Deltic* was short of space and EE feared that if BR insisted on two exhausters and larger capacity train-heating steam generator, much redesigning and increase in locomotive length was likely. The congested cab would make it difficult to accommodate AWS equipment, and the provision of a toilet (which EE tried to argue out of the BR requirement) would be a problem due to lack of space. Buffer standout alterations would require considerable nose-end redesign.

On aesthetics, EE thought reasonable eye-appeal and ease of manufacture would not be appreciated by stylists, but hoped that they could be satisfied if they were allowed to be '. . . let loose on the painting or remove the three "streamlines" from the nose ends.'

The prototype *Deltic* engines had been found too sensitive to high ambient temperatures – indeed, the radiators were inadequate – so Napier had to resolve this with the radiator manufacturers. On the electrical side the control cubicle had to be reduced in width to improve gangway access and leave space for AWS equipment. Experience with the prototype had made some equipment redundant and able to be eliminated. It was hoped that the electrical machines, conduit runs, and batteries could remain unchanged.

EE exercised caution in quoting delivery times to BR, basing this on the problems in altering the mechanical design and keeping within BR restrictions. However, in November 1957 VF quoted EE for 23 sets of mechanical parts similar to the prototype locomotive, and four spare bogies, regardless of the outcome of negotiations with BR on modifications.

On 3 December English Electric representatives met R. C. Bond and E. S. Cox of BR; the outcome was many modifications requiring a lot of new drawings. These included new design of underframe to meet loading gauge requirements, revision of cab equipment and layout, and a larger train-heating steam generator, at a design cost of £30,000. English Electric in its own interest had to provide a new main generator in view of the unsatisfactory operation at times of the original design, and new traction motor frames.

With the Vulcan Foundry estimate for mechanical parts of £155,000 per locomotive, EE had a basis for discussions with BR, but in view of the modifications, thought it impossible to deliver the first locomotive before the end of 1959 even if the 'go-ahead' were given by the end of 1957. On the list of modifications made in October 1957 approval was given by BR, with the following five exceptions:

A4. BR agreed to one exhauster per locomotive.

A5. Locomotive to negotiate 4- not $4\frac{1}{2}$-chain curves.

A6. Train-heating steam generating capacity to be 2,800lb/hr.

A8. No decision on fuel capacity – BR CM&EE decision awaited.

A18. No decision on water softening – BR CM&EE decision awaited.

The next problem to hold up design progress was the question of nose-end gangway connections. R. C. Bond for the BTC said that gangways must be provided, in view of the use of the locomotives to replace class A4 Pacifics with corridor tenders on non-stop King's Cross–Edinburgh Flying Scotsman services, and the necessity to change locomotive crew with the relief crew carried on the train. Some confusion arose when it was suggested that EE could fit the same gangway as fitted to Class 40, which was for inter-locomotive access, not locomotive to train. The question had been resolved to R. C. Bond's previous requirements that gangways were not necessary, and the revision would mean drastic redesign and resiting of equipment to accommodate the gangways. EE was also in doubt as to the type of gangways required by Bond – did he want Class 40 type, or carriage type gangways as fitted to the A4 tenders? If the locomotive type were fitted, a special adaptor plate would have to be carried by all the Deltic locomotives to make up the difference in height between it and the standard carriage gangway. The installed power of the Deltic locomotives was such that multiple-unit working was unlikely, and inter-Deltic connections were not necessary. If R. C. Bond wanted access to the train a full height carriage type gangway was needed, resulting in a higher central nose section which would seriously impair the view from the cab, and either type of gangway would cause difficulties in housing route indicator boxes. EE also enquired why the spare crew could not travel in the trailing cab of the locomotive instead of in the train, and pointed out that as no gangways were being fitted to the 100 3000hp AC

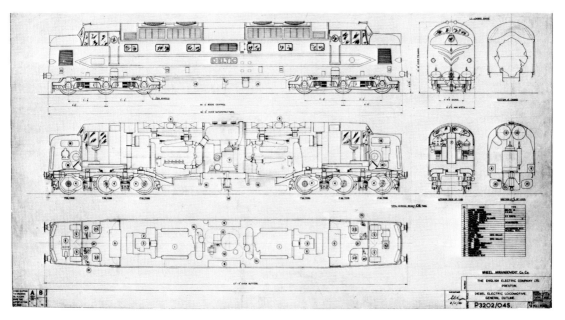

General arrangement of prototype *Deltic* locomotive. (*GEC Traction Ltd*)

electric locomotives being built for BR, which
could presumably take over the East Coast Main
Line when electrified, there was no reason why
the comparative Deltic locomotives should have
gangways. In March 1958 the ER general
manager, to whom the question had been passed,
decided that gangways were not required.

Contract preparations continued, efforts being
made to incorporate all the remaining
modifications, not the least of which was the
requirement to negotiate a 4-chain curve, which
meant that the underframe had to be decreased
across the main longitudinal members to allow for
the wheel throwover from 3ft 1½in. on the
prototype to be reduced to 2ft 10½in. on the new
locomotives. This presented the problem of power
unit mounting in the frame and whether it would
foul the main members.

General arrangement of Class 55 Deltic locomotive.
(*GEC Traction Ltd*)

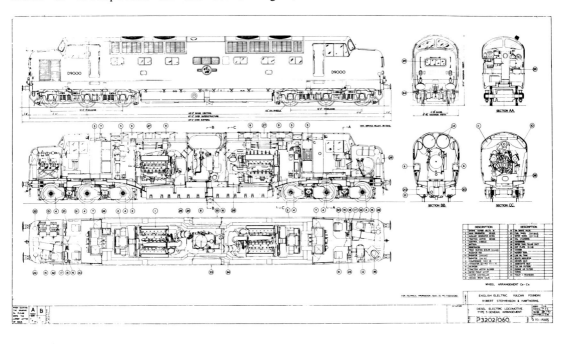

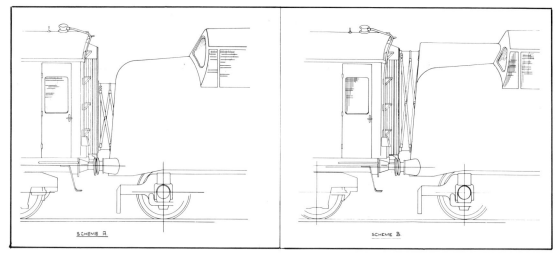

Sketches showing the two schemes for fitting nose end gangway connections in the Class 55 Deltic locomotives. Scheme A – locomotive type gangway; Scheme B – passenger type gangway, both coupled to a standard Mk I passenger carriage. (*Brian Webb collection*)

By 12 March 1958 the number of locomotives had been reduced from 23 to 22 and the contract was being prepared for signing. On 28 March 1958 English Electric quoted £3,410,000 for 22 locomotives, which was accepted by the BTC on 1 May 1958. The stated delivery period was the first locomotive on 30 March 1960 and two per month until the final locomotive on 15 March 1961. Delivery delay damages according to contract could give BR £511,000.

In July 1958 an EE/BR meeting at Doncaster tried to thrash out the outstanding problems but it was not until later in the month that the loading gauge questions were settled:

1. Locomotives to be built to a maximum height of 12ft 11in instead of 13ft 1in.
2. To avoid route and station platform restrictions, the bodyside contour had to be limited to 7ft 10½in at all points below 4ft 1in above rail level.
3. The buffers with 5ft 8in centres exceeded the L1 gauge by 1½in each way owing to locomotive throw-over. Only slight reduction in buffer heads was possible if buffer-locking was to be avoided.
4. The radiused underside outer corners of the fuel tanks were to be checked to ensure that they did not foul L1 at maximum tyre wear conditions.

The end of November 1958 saw agreement reached by compromises on both sides, and although this restricted the locomotives in some aspects, the results were accepted.

One feature of test running with the prototype *Deltic* was the high noise levels both inside and outside the locomotive. On such a run during April 1958 a reading of 120 decibels (dBA) in the engine room, 103dBA in the driving cab with the engine room door open, and 100dBA with the door closed, were recorded at about 60mph with both engines at full output. The BTC was concerned about the noise and EE had to try to ensure that the new Deltics were being designed to a noise level of 80dBA, pointing out that 80dBA had been recorded in a BR diesel power car passenger saloon which appeared quite comfortable to passengers. The easiest way to isolate the locomotive crew from noise was to move the cab to the front of the locomotive, thus putting a compartment between engine room and cab. As far as the Deltics were concerned, EE required the locomotives to have the nose/cab configuration so this solution was ruled out. The noise problem was to assume large proportions once the locomotives entered service.

Route indicators for use on locomotives and multiple-units on BR were approved during 1958. Standardisation on a 4-digit number/letter system, initially designed for the highly-standardised cabs of the first 100 BR AC locomotives, had to be applied to diesel locomotives with a great variety of front-end designs, some with and some without gangway doors, and presented a number of problems. The BR Deltic design consultants, Messrs Wilkes & Ashmore, were responsible for the boxes in their various arrangements.

The abandonment during 1958 of the prototype *Deltic* bogie in favour of a much smaller wheelbase bogie of completely different design, but standard with that to be used on the forthcoming EE Type 3 1750hp Co-Co locomotives for BR, raised severe doubts within the BTC. J. F. Harrison was convinced that the original bogie should be retained as it had ridden well at speed, and doubts were expressed about the ability of the short wheelbase bogie to achieve similar results. EE had to comply with the 4-chain curve requirement imposed by BR and was sure that the new bogie was quite suitable, persisting with it for the new locomotives.

The prototype *Deltic* bogie had a 14ft 4in wheelbase and was designed to negotiate $5\frac{1}{3}$ chains radius and, owing to the larger sweep of the wheels on right- and left-hand curves (including bolster throwover), and to provide reasonable clearance to the locomotive underframe members, it was essential to reduce bogie wheelbase.

The new design of traction motor with four-poles instead of six-poles on the prototype *Deltic* gave a short motor nose swing radius, and as three traction motors were mounted on each bogie this permitted a considerable reduction in wheelbase.

The section and strength of the bogie transoms employed on the prototype was retained, but opportunity was taken with the shorter wheelbase to reduce weight and thus offset the additional weight of the items required by BR on the locomotives, namely, larger train-heating steam generator, toilet, AWS equipment, and dead man's equipment. The reduced wheelbase decreased the moment of inertia, so reducing flange forces and rail wear. Shorter bogies had enabled the accommodation of fuel and water tanks of increased capacity between the bogies. BR did finally accept the bogie in 1959, obtaining a useful standardisation facility with the EE Type 3 and the much later Class 50 BR locomotives.

The main generator of the Type 5 was shorter in length but of larger diameter than that on the prototype *Deltic*. Being self-ventilated, no air-duct was required. The generator was no longer directly driven at 1500 rev/min, but to make flashovers less likely step-down gears were introduced between the engine and generator, which gave an armature speed of 1125 rev/min.

In early 1958 EE decided to develop a new 4-pole traction motor to replace the EE 526A 6-pole motor. The new motor, EE type 538A, would have a larger axle diameter fitting, easier accessibility to

View into No 2 end nose compartment from Class 55 cab, showing congestion caused by installed equipment and indicating the problems should nose gangway connections have become necessary. Visible equipment from left are part of traction motor blower, WC and fold-away wash basin for locomotive crew, and part of air compressor. (*GEC Traction Ltd*)

brushes and commutator, and shorter gear centres and swing radius. This motor would be fitted to the BR Deltic locomotives. The comparison of the two motors was as follows:

	Prototype Deltic	Class 55
Type of motor	EE 526A	EE 538A
Number of poles	6	4
Armature diameter	19in	17in
Core length	16in	16in
Pole pitch	9.95in	13.35in
Length of commutator face	6in	4.75in
Commutator diameter	15.5in	13.5in
Speed at continuous rating	830 rev/min	675 rev/min
Air gap	0.168in	0.25in
Weight complete with gears	6,000lb	5,800lb

The prototype *Deltic* had four rather small traction motor blowers. Lack of space to accommodate larger ones meant they were arranged to cool the generators also. However, the BR Deltics were to have only two traction motor

Class 55 cooling module on the floor at Vulcan Foundry. This unit contains side mounted oil and water coolant radiators, radiator fans, and between the fans the header tank. (*GEC Traction Ltd*)

blowers, and in this case the new type of generator was not to be cooled by the blowers. A fundamental feature of the Deltic locomotives is the method used to accommodate the blowers and their associated ducting. Dual-purpose bogie bolsters of box construction are used as ducts for the air to the traction motors. This was possible by adopting weight-carrying side bearers and a hollow bogie pivot which took air to the bolster. Some argument as to whether four or two blowers should be used took place within EE. Advantages claimed for four small blowers was their access and ease of removal through the cab nose doors into the cab; this would not be so with larger blowers, which also would require more space. In May 1958 the Rolling Stock Design Department of EE was instructed to use two traction motor blowers and redesign the air-ducting to suit. At this time the prototype *Deltic* was at Vulcan Foundry and proved useful to the various EE departments in providing information, including that needed for the blower air-ductings. Upon investigation, and from the resulting calculations, it was found that in practice the prototype *Deltic* never produced the theoretical volume of cooling air to its traction motors. The locomotive did not suffer because of this when in service since its work rarely approached the full capacity of the locomotive.

The train-heating steam generator fitted to the BR Type 5 Deltic locomotives, as on other BR diesel locomotives, has proved to be a serious problem. Following the testing of an American Clayton steam generator in the prototype *Deltic*, and the fact that by 1958 EE was building the Clayton generator under licence at the Newcastle-

upon-Tyne works of Robert Stephenson & Hawthorn Ltd (RSH), it was natural that the Clayton should be favoured for use in locomotives built by EE, the Deltic fleet being no exception. EE considered it quite unacceptable that this group product should be rejected in favour of another make of steam generator, being prepared to stand by it and pressing BR to adopt it.

Unfortunately at the time there was no Clayton generator of the size required in rail traction service anywhere, and by March 1958 it was estimated that some six months would elapse before a design with steam production capacity of 2500lb/hr could be ready, being larger than anything Clayton had produced up to that time. BR demanded that all types of steam generator be traction-proved. BR was willing to accept evidence of service overseas, as it had in the case of the Vapor-Clarkson generator, but EE could not offer this for its product. EE was concerned that as it had to guarantee locomotive availability, it would be under a penalty if the generator proved troublesome.

Consultations with Clayton in El Monte, USA, revealed that no steam generator of the capacity needed for the Deltics would be ready, but some were on trial in the USA and in pre-heating trains at stations. Twenty of the EE-built Claytons of 1000lb/hr capacity were to go into North British Locomotive Co diesel-hydraulic locomotives for the Western Region of BR, and in spite of their smaller size would provide useful service experience.

By mid-1959 EE understood that BR was favouring the Spanner MkII steam generator for future locomotives, and the lack of experience with the Clayton type led EE to order Spanner generators for the Deltics. This they did with some reluctance in late 1959, ordering only twelve Spanner MkII type with a specified steam capacity of 2450lb/hr, in the secret hope that half the locomotives could take the Clayton model which had by now been proved, but which needed to be redesigned as it was too large in its American form. To gain immediate traction experience EE Type 4 D248 was fitted with a Spanner MkII unit for use during the winter of 1959–60. The decision to order the Spanner type for the Deltics was done independently of BR, and to some degree strained relations. EE accepted the responsibility, and if the Spanner type failed, had planned the installation of the Stone-Vapor OK 4625 generator which was preferred by BR. Experience with D248 was

Comparison of bogie designs.
Left: Bogie for the prototype *Deltic* locomotive. It has underslung equalising beams with coil bearing-springs and elliptical bolster springs. Air supply for force-ventilation of traction motors is conveyed through the bogie centre-pivot and bolster.
Right: Class 55 bogie. With underslung equalising beams and coil bearing-springs, but with coil bolster springs. Force ventilation similar to the prototype *Deltic.*

evidently satisfactory, for by February 1960 BR authorised EE to fit Spanner MkII generators to all 22 locomotives, this dashing EE hopes of fitting the modified Clayton in half of the locomotives.

The service weight of the Deltic locomotives required that very careful attention be paid to the weight of every item of equipment to be used on them. In February 1959 the projected weight of the Type 5 Deltics was given as 108 tons, so weight reduction was necessary, fortunately at an earlier stage than with Class 23. One aspect of weight reduction was the need to use hydraulic buffers, which were only made with circular heads of 22in diameter, spaced at 5ft $7\frac{3}{8}$in centres at 3ft $5\frac{1}{2}$in above rail level, and thus infringed the loading gauge on throwover on a 6-chain curve. The buffers saved 6 cwt of Deltic weight, so to retain them EE asked permission to raise the buffers to 3ft $6\frac{1}{2}$in above the rail, one inch above standard, and at 5ft 7in instead of 5ft 8in centres. As it finally turned out, oval-headed buffers of conventional type were fitted, these having $22\frac{3}{8}$in x 14in heads at the above spacings.

The axles of the prototype *Deltic* were hollow for weight saving and proved reliable, so were chosen by EE for the BR Deltics. BR preferred solid axles which EE said would add $6\frac{1}{2}$ cwt to the locomotive weight. It was feared that BR's

insistence would slow design work but in October 1959 BR agreed to hollow axles.

During the production of the Type 5 loco-motives BR thought that some form of visual warning device was required in view of the high-speed operation of the locomotives. Hence, as in the case of today's High-Speed Trains, which have high-power headlamps, a lamp was chosen. BR desired a flashing lamp and after much thought J. Stone & Co of Deptford produced one which appeared to fit the bill. It was an adaptation of a flasher unit used on marine buoys, and it was demonstrated in daylight to EE and BR at Stone's Charlton sports ground. Of one million candlepower, the flashes were of 10 microseconds' duration, with two flashes per second from a xenon lamp giving pure white light. The device would not fit inside any of the locomotive's standard lamp fittings, so it was fitted in the centre of the nose just above the buffer beam. By this time building of the locomotives at VF was well advanced, so fitting the lamp and wiring was difficult to incorporate, made doubly so by the late decision to include the lamp and the delay in receiving supplies. In November 1960 Stone was able to supply a set of equipment for one end of a locomotive, and BR let EE hold back the first locomotive D9000 for fitting. One lamp was to be put at the 'London end' but holes had already been cut at both ends of the locomotive. The lamp unit arrived at the very end of December, with a second promised by the end of January 1961. The flashing lamp was experimental, but EE was instructed to wire all locomotives for it. D9000 was fitted, and on 15 March 1961 tested on the ER main line near Hadley Wood. In April the BTC decided to abandon the experiment and EE was instructed to discontinue wiring further locomotives. The lamp was removed from D9000, and the apertures plated over.

CHAPTER 5

CLASS 55 DELTIC AESTHETICS

In common with other locomotive builders, not all senior staff at English Electric welcomed the appointment by the BR design panel of an industrial design consultant to advise on the Class 55 styling. The consultant was Mr E. G. M. Wilkes, FSIA, of Wilkes & Ashmore, appointed in mid-1958. Wilkes had been concerned with other BR locomotives but his intervention, bearing in mind the existing problems relating to Class 55 design, was not particularly popular with EE.

Wilkes was appointed to cover general exterior appearance, as well as inner cab design. The appearance of the locomotives had to be subordinate to:

1. The functional arrangement of the locomotive.
2. The strength of the locomotive.
3. Accessibility of equipment for inspection and maintenance.

Wilkes criticised the prototype *Deltic* on a number of counts:

1. Depth of the driver's windscreen.
2. Shape of the locomotive nose-ends.
3. Circular windows in the cab doors.
4. Lack of uniformity of the bodyside cantrail louvres near the cab doors.

EE agreed to assist the design panel, convinced that improvement in the appearance was possible without too much alteration, provided that EE mechanical design staff were consulted and their approval gained. By the time all those at EE had been circularised with the aims of the project, various stances (some hard) were adopted and expounded. EE urged its staff to resist radical changes, although they would no doubt be able to meet many of the stylist's requirements in view of the considerable modification being made in the overall locomotive design.

EE desired to meet Wilkes quickly, and on 19 October 1958 he and G. Williams, the BTC design officer, met EE at Preston. By this time EE had revised the bodyside design with a pronounced curvature to meet loading gauge requirements, discarded the aluminium bodyside mouldings, and altered the shape of the nose ends. Wilkes spoke at length on the locomotive and introduced the idea

of a wrap-round windscreen upsetting EE, which described this as a Vauxhall *Victor*-like proposal, referring to the car maker's most ugly and corrosion-prone model of that decade. EE was keen to see that the attitudes of the motor industry with its rapidly-changing models were not introduced into locomotive design!

EE decided this wrap-round screen must go, time and effort being expended to this end. The impracticability of forward-sloping cab windows, pillars, problems of fitting, maintaining, replacing curved glass panels, gained BR support, too. BR agreed that the wrap-round screen was a costly matter with a production run of only 22 locomotives, special tooling being likely to be as much as £1,000 per locomotive. BR pointed out the difficulties in matching accurately the curvature of the glass, the frame, and body structure, without breakage, not to mention possible breakage in service due to racking and flexing of the superstructure, and the resultant difficult replacement and expense of curved glass.

In January 1959 at a meeting in Doncaster the EE case was refuted when Wilkes suggested glass-fibre for complex cab areas, to take the curved screen in a separate frame. A scheme was presented by Wilkes involving redesign of the nose ends, EE having been working for some three months to the earlier design submission, which the company had assumed would be only slightly altered. The screen was retained and supported by the design panel, but not by EE or BR. EE, however, agreed to examine the implications and advise the BTC on the additional costs, extension of delivery dates etc, pointing out that redesign of the locomotive to the rear cab bulkhead would be necessary.

By now it was felt that the six months of industrial design work was dominating the scene and that arbitration was required to resolve the situation. Accordingly, a meeting was held on 19 January at the BTC headquarters in London. Interestingly, E. S. Cox as chairman told EE, BR and the BTC design panel and Wilkes that neither the original contract nor specification referred to any modifications arising from external styling.

There were two proposals for the treatment of the Class 55 nose and cab area.
Top: Designer's drawing for nose and cab treatment as originally conceived, with square forward-sloping nose complete with train nameboard box with integrated marker lights, route indicator box, nose-top air intake. The cabside front pillar slopes forward to accommodate a three-section windscreen with wrap-round. Note horizontal handrail and footstep across nose front.
Bottom: Slightly revised design in model form with less slope to cab pillar and no wrap-round to windscreen; note train nameboard in position. (*Courtesy of E. G. M. Wilkes*)

The points at issue were cab window treatment, and the shape of the nose-ends. Wilkes explained that his revised nose design was to reduce the optical effect of the high nose by using a forward sloping or re-entrant angle, and obtain a better integration between the appearance of the front windows and cabside windows. To achieve this he recommended the wrap-round windscreen. Objections raising tooling costs and maintenance, plus delivery delays due to redesign, together with visibility problems due to random reflections, were expounded. A model of the locomotive as proposed was studied and all agreed that Wilkes' design certainly achieved his aims, but that there were practical difficulties — gold-film demisting

could not be applied to curved glass, nor were the skills needed to produce the re-entry nose shape (akin to automotive panel-beating) available in locomotive building works.

The meeting reached the following conclusions. Having regard to practical uncertainties in connection with a locomotive, which by agreement was required to attain the highest possible availability, it was agreed that curved glass windscreens would not be used. Accepting this, it was agreed that some modification to the front and side cab windows was still acceptable, provided it could be resolved by EE and Wilkes in fourteen days. The nose shape was to conform to Wilkes' original design of October 1958 which EE had been following. Detailed treatment, in particular the radius of the front top corner of the nose, placing of route indicators, and tail lights, should be finalised by EE and Wilkes within fourteen days. Subject to these being resolved, there would be no increase in costs nor in delivery time.

Within the time allowed Wilkes sent his drawings to EE with these comments:

Windscreen. V-shaped flat glass screen retained. Attempts to move main structural pillar to vertical and join this to the front windows with a corner window set at a high

39

angle proved unsatisfactory due to curvature of the roof. Existing sloping corner pillar retained but the roof intersection lines were slightly adjusted to give a more conventional pillar shape, avoiding the distortion evident on the prototype *Deltic*. The same angle of slope was retained as on the EE drawing and approximately the same angle of 'V'. The 'bonnet' joint was moved forward and it was suggested that both the pillars and front panel be welded to the short scuttle panel and cleaned-up to give a smooth run-in. The prototype *Deltic* had a prominent joint line at the base of the cab front panel and pillars, which was unsatisfactory.

Cab side windows. Particular note was taken of the proportions and shape of the small side window in front of the sliding window, and the fact that both top and bottom front corners of the window were radiused; visually this was important.

Driver's step. Increased in length to line up with the door width.

Indicator boxes. Hopes of using recessed glass abandoned due to plan curvature of the nose front and its backward slope. Curved glass was ruled out for reasons stated, and instead a slightly protruding box with flat glass proposed, but that the corner radii of the glazing rubber had to be a minimum, and distance between the rubber and edges of the box kept constant.

*Lamps, horns, train headboards.*The lamps and horns were arranged alongside each other on the extremities of the nose front headboard plinth. If possible, the lamp bezels and horn grilles should be of similar size and design. A simple flat wooden train nameboard, fitting into the plinth aperture, was proposed, the board being pushed in upwards and allowed to rest on the ledge.

Grab rails. These would be horizontal on the nose front.

Front mounting step. To be combined with the cutaway over the couplings to avoid another separate item.

Colour division. The colour break on the Deltics was visually important in reducing the apparent height of the bodysides, by leading the eye lengthways along the locomotive. The colour break coincided with the centre of the lamp plinth running along the top, so that all the plinth was in the lower colour.

By 3 March 1959 EE had accepted the proposals in principle, subject to minor items,

without it affecting delivery of the locomotives, but Wilkes was not apparently informed of this until May 1959. On 2 June a design meeting at Doncaster between BR and EE made the following decisions:

1. Handrails to be vertical not horizontal.
2. Cabside door handrails to be lengthened so that they could be reached from ballast level.
3. Standard lamp-irons to be fitted at each end of the locomotive above each buffer.
4. Flat plate footsteps to be provided on top of each buffer.
5. Proposed footstep across front of locomotive between buffers to be omitted for safety reasons.
6. Train headboard plinth to be eliminated.
7. Tail lamps to be brought nearer to longitudinal centre line to leave room for lamp irons.
8. Warning horns were too long for mounting inside the nose and would be fitted under the buffer beams.

A copy of the above was sent to Wilkes on 30 June who replied regretting the alterations, especially the nose radius which had been changed on the EE drawings from small to large radius, which it was pointed out would give an old-fashioned appearance to the locomotives. There was no other course than to accept the proposals, having paid due regard to the severe limitations and restrictions imposed by EE and BR. Apart from further sundry alterations, the design work at EE could now proceed, so that the only other concerning the aesthetics were liveries, crests and naming procedures.

In spite of the prestige to be enjoyed by the Deltic fleet, it had been intended (regardless of Wilkes & Ashmore) to paint them plain BR green without lining, and J. F. Harrison restated this in early 1960, adding that a grey roof structure, as on other diesels, was also to be used. The large BR crest, the demi-lion rampant holding a locomotive wheel, in fact the crest from the BTC coat of arms, was to be applied. By the autumn some regional individuality was creeping into the subject of Deltic liveries but T. C. B. Miller, ER Chief Mechanical & Electrical Engineer, firmly restated on 30 September that the livery would follow the EE Class 40 pattern and use the large crests. However, it had been decided to paint the first locomotive LNER apple green, and a sample panel with black-and-white lining was sent to VF, the

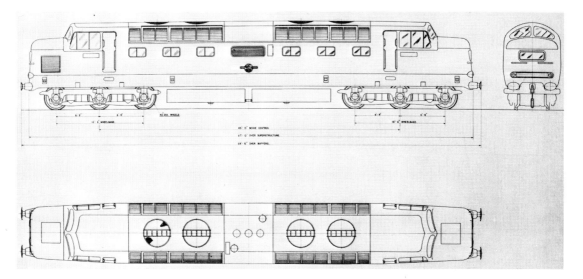

English Electric outline drawing based on E. G. M. Wilkes' third and final compromise design for Class 55. In practice EE dropped the train headboard holder and the nose-front horizontal handrails. (*GEC Traction Ltd*)

lining to be omitted. Consideration was given to extending the livery to the whole fleet, but on 25 October the instruction was cancelled in favour of plain BR green again, in spite of painting having already begun on D9000.

A few days later the Wilkes two-tone green was reinstated and was to be put into practice as soon as possible. The specification was:

Locomotive body – Standard BR locomotive green.

A rare view of D9000 (D9001 was used for the official photograph) at Vulcan Foundry on 28 February 1961. Note high-power flashing headlight above buffer beam in this No 1 end view; it was fitted at both ends. This illustrates Class 55 in its original form when new. (*GEC Traction Ltd*)

Lower body sill – From bottom edge of body to joint line coinciding with bottom of forward nose louvres, light green to BSS2660 5-063.

Cab superstructure – Light grey colour (aluminium paint considered initially).

Roof – BS2660 9-101 Grey.

Fuel tank – Locomotive green.

Bogies – Black.

Rumours of Garter blue and maroon liveries (maroon for the East Coast!) are not supported by factual documentation and one wonders if the latter idea arose from the red-oxide anti-corrosive paint which could have been used on the Class 55 locomotives when being primed during construction at VF, or whether someone used the wrong colour. The crest originally proposed was like that used on the 100 AC electric locomotives then being delivered, but whether of cast aluminium or a transfer is not quite clear. EE was told to paint on the first crest by hand, so the crest was obviously not the standard transfer one.

No 2 end view of D9001 when new at Vulcan Foundry. Note variation in kicking plate on body side at cab door steps compared to D9000, and large BR crest on bodyside prior to naming. (*GEC Traction Ltd*)

With D9000 painted plain green at Vulcan Foundry, EE stated that it would use the two-tone livery as soon as possible and apply the standard large crest in the centre of the bodysides. In spite of this, all the locomotives were handed-over to BR in two-tone green, and then the problem of naming arose. The Eastern Region was quick off the mark, choosing racehorse names in the LNER tradition. The plates were to be placed centrally on the bodysides, making removal of the crest necessary. Some discussion about whether BR or EE should fit nameplate mounting pads, resulted in the former being chosen; being aluminium castings, the plates were easily fixed by bolts. Locomotives D9001, D9003, D9007 and D9009 had their large crests removed before naming at Doncaster, and

Naming ceremony performed on Scottish Region locomotive D9000 *Royal Scots Grey* at Edinburgh Waverley on 18 June 1961, prior to the locomotive taking the up Flying Scotsman to King's Cross.

small crests applied at VF, but in the absence of a naming policy for the NER and ScR locomotives, large bodyside crests were applied to their locomotives.

When the yellow warning panel was applied Wilkes suggested a wrap-round panel around the nose to the leading edge of the nose-side louvres so that the panel would be integrated into the locomotive design. His advice was not followed and a small nose-front rectangular panel applied. Without doubt the locomotives lost some 'eye appeal' when repainted in the all-over rail-blue/yellow nose livery as part of the corporate identity programme – the blanket approach, regardless of design consultant's efforts. Fortunately, with ER approval, Finsbury Park depot gave its 'racehorses' white cab surrounds in 1979, and this made a world of difference, but how nice it would have been if the BR rail grey had been applied to the bodyside sills, too. Finally from 1979 York depot's Class 55s have been given the City of York coat-of-arms on their cabsides – a nice touch of individuality.

In 1979 the Friends of the National Railway

Return to original livery – almost. 55002 *King's Own Yorkshire Light Infantry* in two-tone green but with 1980-pattern full yellow warning panel, TOPS numbering, and City of York coat of arms above number, at the National Railway Museum, York, on 13 December 1980. (*Roger Newling-Goode*)

Museum approached BR offering a major contribution to the repainting of No 55002 (selected for the National Collection when withdrawn) in the original two-tone green livery with early BR crests, but retaining the later all-over yellow cab fronts for safety reasons. This was agreed in due course, and on 14 October 1980 the locomotive entered Doncaster works for its scheduled intermediate repair and repainting in green livery. The locomotive was moved from Doncaster to York during the night of 11 December 1980 and a short ceremony conducted by the ER general manager on the next day to 'hand-over' the locomotive, after which it worked the 14.10 train from York to King's Cross. After withdrawal, the locomotive will become part of the National Collection.

CLASS 55
NUMBERS, NAMES AND NAMING DATES

Original No	New No	Name	Date Named	Location Where Named
D9000	55022	*Royal Scots Grey*	18.6.62	Edinburgh
D9001	55001	*St Paddy*	7.61	Doncaster
D9002	55002	*The King's Own Yorkshire Light Infantry*	4.4.63	York
D9003	55003	*Meld*	7.61	Doncaster
D9004	55004	*Queen's Own Highlander*	23.5.64	Inverness
D9005	55005	*The Prince of Wales' Own Regiment of Yorkshire*	8.10.63	York
D9006	55006	*The Fife & Forfar Yeomanry*	5.12.64	Cupar
D9007	55007	*Pinza*	22.6.61	Doncaster
D9008	55008	*The Green Howards*	30.9.63	Darlington
D9009	55009	*Alycidon*	21.7.61	Doncaster
D9010	55010	*The King's Own Scottish Borderer*	8.5.65	Dumfries
D9011	55011	*The Royal Northumberland Fusiliers*	28.5.63	Newcastle
D9012	55012	*Crepello*	4.9.61	Doncaster
D9013	55013	*The Black Watch*	16.1.63	Dundee
D9014	55014	*The Duke of Wellington's Regiment*	22.10.63	Darlington
D9015	55015	*Tulyar*	13.10.61	Doncaster
D9016	55016	*Gordon Highlander*	28.7.64	Aberdeen
D9017	55017	*The Durham Light Infantry*	29.10.63	Durham
D9018	55018	*Ballymoss*	24.11.61	Doncaster
D9019	55019	*Royal Highland Fusilier*	11.9.65	Glasgow Central
D9020	55020	*Nimbus*	12.2.62	Doncaster
D9021	55021	*Argyll & Sutherland Highlander*	29.11.63	Stirling

Note: Naming locations are railway stations, except for the ER locomotives which were named upon or soon after delivery at Doncaster works. Locomotives D9000, D9004, D9006, D9008, D9010, D9013, D9014, D9016, D9019, and D9021 also fitted with regimental badges during their service life. Number series D1000–21, D1500–21, D6000–21 were all considered before D9000–21 was finally selected.

CHAPTER 6

CLASS 55 THE DELTIC CONTRACT AND DELIVERY

The maintenance and performance contract between British Rail and English Electric for the Class 55 Deltics was dated 28 March 1958 and was quite a hefty document which can only be summarised here.

The contract provided for a maintenance period of five years to commence on the delivery of the first locomotive or on such other date as might be agreed upon. During the maintenance period the BTC (BR) undertook to carry out at its own expense, under the supervision and to the reasonable satisfaction of EE, all such period maintenance of diesel engines, electrical equipment and mechanical parts described in a maintenance schedule appended to the contract.

EE undertook to carry out repair and overhaul of major components detailed in the appendices of the contract, this being work not covered by the provisions set out above. EE would do this at its expense unless the work was due to negligence on the part of the BTC (BR), which would then bear the cost.

The locomotive the East Coast main line wanted and got. A September 1961 shot of D9003 *Meld* at King's Cross waiting at depart on a Leeds express. The Finsbury Park "racehorse" locomotives were the first Class 55 to receive names. The centrally-placed plates required the repositioning of the BR crest, so smaller crests were applied below the locomotive numbers. (*Brian Webb collection*)

All work of or connected with maintenance, repair or overhaul, in addition to that provided for above, would be carried out by the BTC under supervision and to EE satisfaction. EE would bear the cost unless BTC (BR) were held responsible for the work, due to negligence. EE undertook to transport to and from the EE works any major components/equipment necessary for maintenance, repair or overhaul carried out by EE, costs to be borne by the party at whose expense the work was carried out.

Information would be exchanged between EE and BTC (BR) to establish that costs charged were reasonable. EE undertook to maintain at its expense specified stocks of major components and it was agreed that any replacement components fitted to locomotives during the maintenance period would then become BTC (BR) property, and the components removed would become EE property. EE also agreed to provide and replace at its own expense specified consumable parts, and parts subject to wear and tear.

EE agreed, with certain safeguards, to ensure that the 22 locomotives would be able and available to operate an aggregate diagrammed mileage of 4.5 million miles per year during the five-year maintenance contract. It was stipulated that no single locomotive should be diagrammed to work more than 220,000 miles annually. In

D9005, then unnamed, passing past Skelton Engineers yard, York, with an up express on Bank Holiday Monday, 7 August 1961. This picture illustrates the powerful appearance of Class 55. (*Brian Webb*)

consideration of EE obligations on this, the BTC (BR) would pay EE a maintenance charge during the maintenance period of each locomotive. The charges would be over five 12-calendar monthly periods on a sliding scale, ranging from £720 per month for the first twelve months to £600 per month for the last, with provision for appropriate reductions for reduced mileage run. A clause was also included to provide for adjustments in these charges, by agreement, in the light of variations in costs of labour or materials.

Upon termination of the contract at the end of the maintenance period the BTC (BR) would purchase from EE the stocks of major components held by the firm. Provision was made for rebates to

D9007 *Pinza* takes a 12-coach load southwards past York Holgate Bridge station on 7 August 1961. (*Brian Webb*)

the BTC (BR) in the event of the diagrammed mileage not being attained for reasons outside the control of EE or BTC (BR).

The maintenance contract started on 22 March 1961, the date that the first locomotive was recorded as taken over, and ran until its termination on 21 March 1966.

By November 1959 discussions were under way between BR and EE on the maintenance contract for the Deltic locomotives. EE was hoping that it would be able to deliver the first locomotive to BR one month earlier than contracted, in April 1960. However, by August the first locomotive was still under construction at Vulcan, and BR was asking questions. In mid-September 1960 EE said that manufacturing difficulties made it necessary to revise Deltic deliveries. Deliveries were to start now in December 1960 with two locomotives, continuing until May 1961 with three locomotives, and then two per month until September with the twenty-second locomotive in October 1961. EE had decided to 'play safe' and hoped to redeem itself by delivering three locomotives by the end of 1960. For the BTC J. F. Harrison enquired if

The high mileages stipulated in the Class 55 contract required their use on the fastest high-mileage schedules. Here D9020 *Nimbus* backs through Holloway to King's Cross prior to working the northbound centenary run of The Flying Scotsman on 18 June 1962. The locomotive has roof-mounted warning horns and small yellow warning panel on nose front. (*J. F. Aylard*)

Deltic deliveries could be speeded-up to finish by the end of July 1961, EE saying this was possible if delivery of EE Type 4 2000hp locomotives could be slowed down.

On 9 October 1961 when deliveries were under way, EE set out under two categories their reasons for the delay.

Category A. Delays caused by BTC and BR
1. Loading gauge – no clear instructions on interpretation of L1/C1 loading gauge. BTC/BR argued for the more stringent gauge, while EE pressed for a more liberal profile. Much time was expended before EE advice and the large gauge was agreed to.
2. Styling – time wasted producing special drawings and design panel discussions.
3. Provision of gangway connections – this proposal wasted time until it was decided it was not possible to accommodate gangways in such a tightly-packed locomotive.
4. Fuel capacity – the prototype *Deltic* carried 800 gallons of fuel, the BR Deltics 900 gallons. Space and weight problems took time to resolve so that a larger fuel tank could be fitted.
5. AWS equipment – a major problem to find space to accommodate this compulsory BR fitment. The prototype Deltic had no AWS.

Category B. Delays due to EE
Nearly all major changes fell in this category – new engines, exhaust system, radiators, fans, generators, traction motors, control gear, and auxiliaries. Apart from water pick-up gear salvaged from the prototype *Deltic*, all other drawings for mechanical parts were new. The 6-ton increase in locomotive weight caused by the above was not allowed by BR, so 'lightening' exercises also took time.

The train-heating installation design was delayed due to indecision on the type of steam generator to fit.

EE felt that all Category B changes were necessary to provide BR with the best locomotive possible.

All this was prompted by the threat in late September 1961 by the BTC that the late delivery of the Deltics had involved the railways in a loss, and that the Commission had to consider the question of claiming damages in accordance with the terms of the Deltic contract. In the end the episode ended satisfactorily and no damages were claimed. The delivery dates were as follows, but not adhered to:

Locomotive No	Contract delivery date
D9000	30.4.60
D9001	15.5.60
D9002	30.5.60
D9003	15.6.60
D9004	30.6.60
D9005	15.7.60
D9006	31.7.60
D9007	15.8.60
D9008	31.8.60
D9009	15.9.60
D9010	30.9.60
D9011	15.10.60
D9012	31.10.60
D9013	15.11.60
D9014	30.11.60
D9015	15.12.60
D9016	31.12.60
D9017	15.1.61
D9018	31.1.61
D9019	15.2.61
D9020	28.2.61
D9021	15.3.61

As locomotive deliveries proceeded, a careful check was kept of locomotive mileages, both by EE representatives at the depots to which Class 55 were allocated and at Doncaster works; in the latter case they had an office in King's Arcade, Doncaster, so that failures and work done on Class 55 could be assessed to ascertain whose responsibility it was to correct them. This arrangement provoked much argument and correspondence between EE and BR.

In the first case only part performance/mileages were booked so that, for example, on 12 August 1961 locomotives D9000–10 were in traffic and had covered a total mileage of 190,690 miles since new. Individual locomotive mileages varied from 3,893 to 40,617 miles, depending mainly on how long they had been in service. A total of 3,858 lost miles was logged against these eleven locomotives. On 4 November 1961 with seventeen locomotives in service the total mileage was 609,828, with 14,508 lost miles.

As the 6-year contract progressed towards its termination, there were still continual

With its 'D' number prefix removed and in rail blue livery, 9010 *The King's Own Scottish Borderer*, stands at Haymarket depot in January 1973 after completing two million miles (3.2 million kilometres) in just under 12 years of revenue-earning service, a world record. Note ventilation louvres above nameplate to provide additional ventilation for the locomotive batteries, nose-top warning horns fitted to all locomotives, and ETH jumper cable above right-hand buffer. (*GEC Traction Ltd*) *Ltd*)

discrepancies over who was responsible for what. In April 1964 it was stated that the main reasons for lost mileage caused by BR were: Spanner steam generators putting locomotives out of traffic in winter months; preparations for naming ceremonies on NER and ScR locomotives; excessive time taken in depot examinations; failure of locomotives to take up their booked workings due to operating incidents which affect all types of locomotive.

On some items BR and EE agreed to share responsibility, for example, batteries, bogies, steam generator and so on, but not necessarily on a 50–50 basis. In the third year of the contract's first 4-weekly period 7,592 miles (24%) were lost, attributable to EE, 22,236 (70%) lost due to BR, and 1,923 (6%) were under investigation, making a total of 31,751 miles lost in four weeks. This was marginally worse than the same period in 1963, and again sparked off arguments.

J. F. Harrison, BR CM&EE, thought that BR was taking on responsibilities which should be those of EE, but this was erroneous as miles lost due to EE had dropped in the first three years from 8.8 to 3.2%, while those lost due to BR had only dropped from 8.8 to 7.8%. EE had overcome most of its troubles; BR had not, and it was difficult to see how weather conditions, collisions, derailments, delays preventing locomotives taking up their booked workings, and depot examinations taking too long, could be resolved.

In May 1965 the following figures covering the first two years were given:

Details	Year 1	Year 2	Totals for 2 years
Diagrammed miles	4,401,424	4,519,640	8,921,064
Miles lost due to BR	386,015	354,568	740,583
	4,015,409	4,165,072	8,180,481
Miles run 22 locos	3,651,506	3,960,683	7,612,189
Miles run DP2 in lieu		62,719	62,719
Diagrammed miles lost	363,903	141,670	505,573
Miles run by Deltics not Deltic diagrams	22,606	38,792	61,398
Miles lost by Deltics on Deltic diagrams	386,509	180,462	566,971

The gradual deterioration of mileage was attributable in part to the three years' intensive working done by the locomotives, and the resultant increase in time spent in works which was largely responsible for the increased loss of mileage. The shortage of spares and slow delivery of repaired engines from Napier's was EE responsibility.

In the 1965 summer period the total weekly mileage was 91,835 and over twelve weeks 1,102,000 miles. On 28 October 1965 performance statistics for the maintenance contract for the twelve months 15 June 1964 to 12 June 1965 were: miles lost to EE 156,088, to BR 571,300, giving an aggregate of 727,388 miles.

At the termination of the maintenance contract on 21 March 1966 the locomotives' individual total mileages were stated by BR to be:

D9000	827,055	D9011	691,916
D9001	798,830	D9012	715,415
D9002	673,767	D9013	775,180
D9003	813,865	D9014	684,145
D9004	838,624	D9015	729,910
D9005	740,015	D9016	777,192
D9006	832,060	D9017	713,935
D9007	799,147	D9018	705,300
D9008	716,760	D9019	769,833
D9009	763,116	D9020	700,024
D9010	820,218	D9021	646,894

Total mileage 16,533,201.

The second maintenance contract between EE and BR was timed to start on 22 March 1966 and EE wished to limit the company's responsibilities to the repair and overhaul of the Deltic engines only. This was acceptable to BR, but it was agreed that repairs to main and auxiliary generators and traction motors of Class 55 would be done as required by EE on a price list basis and not be part of the contract. Under the contract EE would do work confined to major overhaul or repair arising from normal wear and tear, design modifications, from defective workmanship or materials where, subject to EE decision, an engine change was required.

The amount of work required to be carried out under the terms of the contract was to be at the discretion of EE and include such work, replacement and reconditioning of components as considered necessary. Although EE assumed engine overhaul periodicity as 5000 hours, the tolerance would be 4600–5000 hours. Shopping of Class 55 was based on 2000 and 4000 hours and difficulty would arise in keeping engines in phase with the locomotives. Experiments were in hand to lift the engine figure to 6000 hours.

BR would be responsible for the costs of overhaul and repair work arising from mal-operation or deficiencies in its own maintenance schedules. EE would retain three members of staff, one at King's Cross and two at Doncaster. EE would transport the engines to and from BR works, with BR paying reasonable costs involved. BR agreed to lift out and re-install engines in locomotives to the satisfaction of Napier/EE. Provision was made for fluctuations in material and labour costs.

Payment to EE was at the rate of an agreed sum per engine-hour, BR being responsible for recording these hours weekly. Engine overhaul programmes and provision of spare engines were to be arranged so that not more than one locomotive was out of service at any one time awaiting engines except in circumstances out of the reasonable control of EE. A penalty clause if more than two locomotives were out of service awaiting engines was included, based on the average amount paid per locomotive to EE under the maintenance contract during the previous twelve months for each period of seven days, a figure of two per cent being quoted. This only applied if BR did not plan two locomotives for engine change within two weeks of each other. No more than six locomotives were planned for engine change in any 90-day period, and EE had the right to transfer serviceable engines between locomotives at its discretion.

The contract was for three years, and EE undertook to train sufficient BR staff to undertake

MILEAGE FOR PERFORMANCE PERIOD 18 JUNE 1962 TO 21 MARCH 1966 (3 YEARS 272 DAYS) AS RECORDED BY EE

Period	Contract diagram miles	Aggregate diagram miles	Actual miles	Miles lost due to BR	EE
18.6.62 to 17.6.63	4,500,000	4,422,965	3,651,506	385,097	386,362
18.6.63 to 17.6.64	4,500,000	4,494,123	3,960,683	352,978	180,462
18.6.64 to 17.6.65	4,500,000	4,591,498	3,864,110	571,300	156,088
18.6.65 to 26.3.66	3,412,211	3,301,781	2,616,181	488,962	196,638
Totals	16,912,211	16,810,367	14,092,480	1,798,337	919,550

Deltic engine work to an adequate level by the termination of the contract, as BR required. At the termination of the 3-year engine maintenance contract BR wanted to take over Deltic engine work at Doncaster. To gain experience on this exacting work it was decided to train staff at Napier's on the Class 23 Baby Deltic engines. Unfortunately, this plan came to nought after EE had been involved in much expense, due to the British Railways Board decision to withdraw these locomotives from service.

Accordingly, it was decided that Doncaster would commence Class 55 engine work during the autumn of 1968 and in this way gain the experience to enable complete takeover from EE on 21 March 1969 when the contract expired. The first Doncaster-repaired engine was due off test on 2 May 1969, by which time it had been arranged that Napier would continue to overhaul engines until Doncaster was fully ready to take over the task, Napier doing thirteen engines after the end of the contract.

The argument concerning Class 55 maintenance cost was answered in part by an ER report of autumn 1968, comparing conventional BR locomotive costs with the Class 55.

ER MAINTENANCE COSTS FOR CLASSES 47 AND 55 IN OCTOBER 1968

	Class 47	Class 55
Workshop cost	£1,575,452	£171,076
Depot cost	754,510	84,940
Contractor's cost	—	167,000
	£2,329,962	£423,016
Mileages	13,671,970	2,284,180
Cost per mile	40.8d	44.4d

COMPARABLE LMR MAINTENANCE COSTS FOR CLASS 47 AND 86 AC ELECTRICS AND ER CLASS 55 (CLASS 45 INCLUDED WITH CLASS 47)

	Class 47	Class 86	Class 55
Maintenance cost	49.7d	14.32d	44.4d
Fuel oil/engine oil	13.68d	—	20.8d
Electricity	—	24.3d	—
Overhead line maintenance	—	8.0d	—
Total cost per mile	63.38d	46.62d	65.2d

CHAPTER 7

CLASS 55 THE DELTIC ENGINE IN SERVICE

The Deltic D18-25 engine fitted to the BR Class 55 locomotive is quite different from the Series I Deltic engine used for marine craft propulsion. The redesigned locomotive engine was the Series II with, as its most notable difference, the alterations to the phasing gear casing to enable flange mounting of an EE traction main generator.

The Napier Deltic diesel engine is a diesel engine operating on the 2-stroke cycle, or 2-stroke principle, but with opposed pistons arranged in horizontal and diagonal banks forming an equilateral triangle. The engine is in effect three opposed piston engines, each driving its own crankshaft. The power from each crankshaft is geared to an assembly at the driving end of the engine, via phasing gears which combine the engine power to a common output shaft on the centre line of the engine. On the rail traction engine this shaft drives a main generator.

Additional secondary gearing is provided through the phasing gears to drive auxiliary equipment such as auxiliary generator, cooling fan drive, engine governor, and oil pressure pump. The accompanying diagrams illustrate the main points of the engine.

The engine itself was conceived in 1946. Being sponsored by the British Admiralty for use in naval craft, it was available commercially in 1951 and has subsequently found much use in marine and industrial applications. So far as rail traction is concerned it has proved somewhat disappointing, being used only in the 33 locomotives which form the subject of this book.

The advantages of producing high power from a largely light-alloy built, light weight and compact engine has always been attractive to rail traction engineers, and the Deltic engine provided just that. Class 55 has a total of 57 engines available, 44 of which would normally be included in the locomotives, leaving 13 under overhaul or as spares.

To obtain the necessary engine experience one complete Deltic engine with its EE main and auxiliary generator group was set up and tested at Napier's Liverpool works. The results made it necessary to modify and adjust many items,

notably the engine control system and governor. Further test-house running, simulating the locomotive set up with air intake ducting, exhaust trunking, silencer, coolant radiators, oil-heat exchangers, and mechanically driven cooling fan, was undertaken to assess engine endurance for 1000-hour running.

Following the tests the engine was stripped for examination for wear, damage, malfunction of components and assemblies. It was found that the Barber-Coleman spline assemblies showed signs of fretting (wear), redesign being undertaken together with revised assembly techniques; the output spline suffered from torsional deflections between the hub and the output shaft.

The final engine test before the Class 55 locomotives entered service was done at VF on locomotive D9000. The test included a 100-hour period of idling and full power/accelera-tion/deceleration. Although no problems were experienced, stripping of the test engine again exposed Barber-Coleman spline fretting and also severe cavitational erosion on the outsides of the cylinder liners; this damage was after 750 hours' running and due to the use of raw water coolant instead of the 30/70 glycol/water mixture formulated later. Unfortunately, the urgency of getting the locomotives into service since they were already well behind contract delivery dates (to some extent due to the late delivery of the Deltic engines) meant that Deltic engines likely to have these faults had already been installed in locomotives prior to stripping of the test engine.

Initial service problems with Class 55 resulted in the earlier locomotives being put through the EE works of VF and of RSH at Darlington, where engine changes were made and modified units fitted; sadly, many cases were prompted by engine failures.

As expected, the Barber-Coleman spline began to fail. On one locomotive, D9002, in November 1961 the splines collapsed on one crankshaft phasing gear quillshaft. This gear wheel coupled the crankshaft to the main output drive shaft of the main generator. The Barber-Coleman spline was machined in the form of a taper and combined the

D9000 *Royal Scots Grey* with the up centenary Flying Scotsman pulls away from Edinburgh Waverley after its naming ceremony on 18 June 1962. (*Brian Webb collection*)

advantage of a tapered shaft and parallel splines. The taper served as a location for the driven component on its shaft and the parallel splines transmitted the drive. The gear type coupling was fitted to the quillshaft. Some engine seizures were caused by the locking plate securing the ring nut locating the quillshaft drive gear on the crankshaft failing. Modified locking plates and ring nuts were fitted at engine repairs and to new engines.

Another early problem was with the overspeed trip shutting-down an engine, due to vibration trouble. Similarly, the underspeed switch gave trouble and this was modified to include two switches for more reliable use, as one switch caused unnecessary power failure.

The failure of pistons caused by broken connecting-rods developing small surface cracks resulted in the fitting of differently machined connecting rods.

During November–February 1961–2, following a period of trouble with the radiator fan gearboxes, a reconditioning programme was undertaken by the makers of the gearbox, which were replaced at VF, RSH and Doncaster.

Anyone who has known the Class 55 is aware that the locomotives are prone to the emission of dense engine exhaust smoke with a particular Deltic smell. The problems of this exhaust smoke and its possible elimination were early considered

by EE, Napier and BR; as more Class 55 entered service they began to work sleeping-car trains, this brought many complaints from passengers because the exhaust was drawn into their compartments. In an attempt to overcome this, de-odorants were added to the locomotive fuel, and also to the sleeping-car air filters.

Each Deltic engine has three exhaust manifolds which have to be fed into an exhaust collector box with one outlet to the atmosphere via the silencer; that is, two sets per locomotive.

It was felt that the oil carry-over of the Deltic engines was partly responsible for the fumes. However, this was overtaken by the rapid failure of the exhaust drum tanks themselves, which suffered weld failures at joints after 700–1000 hours' running because the contractor had not annealed the welds. Temporary repairs using pre-loaded bolts and distance-pieces provided time for redesign of the drum tank. The redesign proposed firstly a mild-steel riveted tank of 3/16in, 5/32in or $\frac{1}{8}$in thickness, weighing 241lb, 217lb or 193lb respectively, or as a second option a stainless-steel tank of 170lb weight which would be costly but last longer. BR was pressing for action in early 1962 so a modified tank (MkII) was introduced, incorporating strengthening in addition to annealing of welds. It was hoped to fit all locomotives by the end of May 1962.

The basic problem was the carry-over of engine lubricating oil into the exhaust and exhaust system, a phenomenon which not only caused dense fumes but also sparks and flames to appear

Napier Deltic D18–25 1650hp engine with English Electric 829 main generator and 913 auxiliary generator as used in Class 55.
Key:
1. Auxiliary generator. 2. Take-off gear and shaft drive to roof-mounted radiator fans. 3. AB crankcase. 4. Exhaust collector drum tank. 5. Scavenge blower. 6. CA crankcase. 7. C cylinder bank. 8. Main generator. (*GEC Diesels Ltd*)

from Class 55 exhausts, almost producing some steam locomotive pyrotechnics at night! It was decided to try to drain the carried-over engine oil from the drum tanks by designing a MkIII tank fitted with open oil drain pipes, D9017 being fitted with a pair of these in February 1962. As an alternative, the fitting of an oil-collecting tank to the drain pipes, as opposed to letting the oil drain onto the track, was tried on D9006, which on a King's Cross–Edinburgh run accumulated between a quarter and a half pint of oil. It was reported that there was little significant improvement in the exhaust fumes emitted. By the autumn of 1962 it was being opined that oil carry-over was due mainly to the idling of the engines and was burned-off under hard working

conditions, thus damaging the tanks. EE had doubts that the oil carry-over problem had been correctly diagnosed. The drum tank replacement programme coincided in some cases with an engine change, being done at RSH Darlington or BR Doncaster from January to May 1962.

It is interesting to note that the fitting of new oil seals to the Deltic engine scavenge-blowers did effect some improvement in exhaust conditions, but they remained much worse than on other BR diesel locomotives. The drum tank drain pipes were removed from mid 1966 and the fumes remain to this day!

Another problem which occurred when Class 55 was on test at VF and after entering service concerned the adjustment of the engine load control system, and many variations on individual locomotives were found and in due course corrected during 1961–2. During the process discussions as to the merit/demerit of the Class 55 Ardleigh engine governor and the Woodward governor took place, and in late 1961 Deltic engine No 406 with a Woodward governor was tested on the Napier test-bed, but no advantage over the

Detail of 18-cylinder engine, showing arrangement of three banks of six cylinders.

Key:

1. BC crankshaft	12. A cylinder block
2. BC crankcase	13. Fuel injection pump
3. Inlet piston	14. Exhaust manifold
4. B cylinder block	15. CA crankcase
5. Exhaust piston	16. CA crankcase cover
6. AB crankcase	17. CA crankshaft
7. AB crankshaft	18. CA flexible drive shaft
8. Connecting rod	19. Castellated ring nut
9. Crankcase tie bolt	20. Cylinder liner
10. Drain oil manifold	21. Cylinder block
11. Air inlet ducts	22. Blower drive shaft

(GEC Diesels Ltd)

modified Ardleigh unit was found. Difficulties with the interchangeability of Deltic engines and governors, particularly with the stability of the latter, were overcome in 1962.

Engine electrical equipment mounted on the engines suffered many defects during 1961–2, mainly due to the destructive effect of the engine on the wiring, micro-switches and instruments, but also due to design deficiencies and equipment not being robust enough for the rigours of rail traction. A re-assessment of the equipment improved the situation and as much equipment as possible was

mounted independently of the engine.

A summary of Class 55 engine failures during the period 2 March 1961 to 25 April 1962 revealed the following: connecting rod failures – 6; de-phasing – 6; fractured liners – 2; miscellaneous failures – 3.

During the testing of D9000 at VF in the period November 1960 to February 1961 very grave misgiving arose on the high noise levels of the Deltic engines, both outside and inside the locomotive, particularly in the drivers' cabs. BR had already formed the opinion that the Baby Deltics were too noisy, and EE feared that the 3300hp locomotive noise would be unacceptable, since it was far worse than on the smaller locomotive.

It was obvious that in spite of careful attention to sound-proofing during design and construction, the situation left much to be desired. Initial sound-proofing consisted of using expanded-rubber compound between inner and outer panelling, filling the void between cab inner and outside panels, filling of the door interiors between the cab and nose compartment, and use of rubber seals on all door edges. Asbestos sound-deadeners were used in the bulkheads of the control cubicle and on the inner side of cab roof panels. Fibreglass (GRP) was used to fill the space over the control cubicles and the bulkhead. The hinged doors between the cabs and the engine room were made of GRP and their internal honeycomb structure filled with vermiculite. The cab flooring was of plywood with an aluminium facing on the underside and 4.5mm linoleum on top. Patent sound absorbents were sprayed inside the doors and covers of the control cubicles. Rubber pads were fitted on the bogie primary and secondary coil springs and on the eight superstructure side-bearers to prevent noise and vibration transmission.

It had to be appreciated that locomotives of such high installed horsepower and with two Deltic high-speed diesel engines, coupled with low locomotive weight and small size, were inherently much noisier than conventional powered locomotives with large medium-speed engines. EE had tried to take all this into account, but following test runs in March 1961 with BR representatives on board, BR stated that cab noise level was unacceptable and that it would appear that little or no sound insulation had been fitted! EE was asked to rectify this as soon as possible, and incorporate the modifications in future locomotives before delivery to BR.

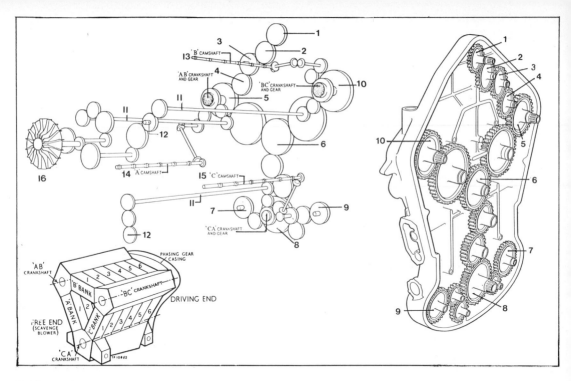

Deltic engine components. *Left:* Diagram of the various drives and driven members passing through the engine to the phasing gear. *Right:* Phasing gears and phasing gear casing coupled to the items in the left-hand diagram.

Key:
1. Auxiliary generator and fan drive
2. Idler gear to 3
3. Govenor drive gear
4. Idler gear to 5
5. AB crankshaft phasing gear
6. Output gear
7. Pressure oil pump gear
8. CA crankshaft phasing gear
9. Scavenge oil pump gear
10. BC crankshaft phasing gear
11. Scavenge blower flexible drive shaft
12. Meter oil pump drive
13. B camshaft
14. A camshaft
15. C camshaft
16. Scavenge blower

Inset bottom left: Perspective sketch showing basic Deltic engine arrangement. (*Brian Webb collection*)

Urgent negotiations between EE and Napier took place with the aim that the fourth locomotive, D9003, due for delivery on 27 March 1961, could be modified. Among the additional noise insulation work was that on the locomotive air intake; the Deltics required 168,000cu ft of air per minute, so it was not an easy task. BR indicated that 80 decibels (DbA) was probably an acceptable noise level in the cabs, but EE thought that 80–100 DbA was a more realistic level, so much more work was needed to achieve the BR figure. By this time locomotive deliveries had progressed, and this resulted in D9006 being chosen for the additional

work, being due for delivery on 23 June 1961 and then testing by EE and Napier.

The improvements on D9006 were to include fitting additional doors at three of the four positions between the cabs and the engine room to reduce noise transmission further. The fourth door could not at first be fitted, due to its proximity to the breakfast cooker unit – the doors were identical to those already fitted but opened the opposite way; lining the engine air-intake ducts with half inch polyurethane foam between air entry and the filters, applying half inch polyurethane foam to steel sealing panels below the control cubicles, and to the underside of the cab floors where removable, and the covering of the rear transverse panels of the control cubicles with sound-insulating material. The cost of this additional work was put at £200, and if tests with D9006 proved successful locomotives under construction would be fitted prior to delivery and those in traffic done retrospectively. An additional noise source was pointed out by the EE Whetstone laboratories, namely the engine phasing gear cases and the scavenge-blowers with their associated ducting. Tests with D9006 showed that the modifications had reduced noise levels by 3 DbA.

The railway trades unions still thought the noise levels too high and in October/November 1961 were complaining about the unreasonable stress being placed on Class 55 crews, who found it difficult to concentrate, communicate with each other, and in hearing warning devices above the noise. Earplugs and ear muffs were therefore useless and it was intimated that crews could start to refuse to work the locomotives unless further improvements were made.

EE did further work on D9006 but pointed out that only marginal improvements were possible due to lack of space and the mass of the required materials inside the locomotive. The further work on D9006 was as follows: sprayed sound-deadening materials inside panelling of body structure between the two cabs including the removable roofs over the engines, inside of steel panels (sides and front bulkheads) of cabs similarly sprayed, one inch thick rubber floor covering laid on top of cab floor linoleum, additional perforated cab ceiling panels placed half an inch below the existing panels with the intervening space filled with sound-insulating material, increased thickness of sound deadener on cubicle covers and doors, and covering of engine room GRP doors with sound barrier mats. It was also decided to fit a partition behind each cab seat to act as combined sound and draught screen, with a folding curtain across the space between them. Further tests with D9006 during January 1962 involving EE, Napier and the British Aircraft Corporation were evidently a success, and the BTC agreed that D9015, the next locomotive due to visit an EE works for engine modifications, should be fitted like D9006. D9015 was to undergo tests before and after the modification to its sound insulation materials. D9006 had not received the folding curtain, but following pre-modification tests on 10 April 1962 D9015 had, when it entered the Darlington works of RSH. While D9015 was at RSH D9021, partly improved in sound insulation when built, had gained some approval from crews.

By October tests with D9015 had been found satisfactory, but noise levels were still in the first octave band and, according to the ER medical officer, above the limit where prolonged exposure could provoke permanent hearing damage. The tests were done on 23 July and then while stationary at RSH works on 13 September 1962. The former date's tests consisted of running on the 07.30 Leeds–King's Cross with D9015 suitably instrumented and with test personnel on board the locomotive, the test being a repetition of that of 10 April. The tests revealed that the April tests gave a noise range of 92–105 DbA, and the July tests 83–102 DbA with all doors and windows closed, but varied considerably as to whether the locomotive was standing or running, and also with certain windows and doors open. It was decided to fit all locomotives similarly to D9015, if possible by May 1963. Interestingly, it was discovered that through an oversight at RSH D9015 had not been fully sound-proofed to specification, but with no adverse effect!

The failure of quill shafts has posed continuous problems and even though design, manufacturing techniques, and material specifications have been changed, they continue to occur, albeit at a more acceptable level. Causes of the failures were hard to define and by 1974 the shafts were in short supply. Tests had been undertaken to find the causes, such as fatigue tests under torsional and bending loads, materials to overcome fretting, fitting of improved dampers, but with little initial improvement. In later 1974 the suggestion that engines running on only seventeen cylinders were causing quill shaft failures was examined and the investigation pinned the problem down to faulty injectors, which when attended to did improve the position, lessening the frequency of failures. In 1977 a stronger quillshaft was introduced which again improved their lives.

Throughout certain periods of Class 55 service life the supply of spare engines has not always been sufficient to meet locomotive requirements. Apart from the need to change engines at classified repair periods, engines often require changing when they give trouble during the intervening time, so a pool of engines should always have been available. The serious engine problems already summarised obviously had an adverse effect on the supply of Deltic engines, the demand being far too unpredictable for accurate planning. The best that could be hoped for was to have as many repaired spare engines as possible in stock at Doncaster works.

By the end of 1962 Napier was approximately 18 days behind schedule due to the replacement rate of cylinder liners being higher than expected; their planning for delivery of five repaired engines per month was to be raised to six as soon as possible. Erosion of liner seatings caused by use of unsuitable coolant water additives was blamed for the fractured liners. By March 1963 the delivery of engines was only three days behind schedule, and the fitting of reconditioned liners well in hand. By late 1964 there was again a shortage of spare engines and Napier, trying to improve deliveries in 1965, suggested that Doncaster works could usefully assist if they could test the engines and thus release the bottleneck at the former's works. Doncaster agreed to do this task until Napier caught up.

Some loss of Class 55 availability from the lack of engines was due to locomotives spending longer periods in works awaiting these, and it took until early 1966 to get engine deliveries back to schedule again. By the summer sufficient spare engines were in stock. A spate of failures soon put this in jeopardy, for by October no spare engines remained. In spite of this, at the end of 1966 the ER locomotives had an average availability of 85%, the NER locomotives 75%, and the ScR locomotives 70%. The total regional fleet mileages since 1961 were 6,964,250, 5,005,040, and 7,091,710 miles respectively. Shortages in 1967 again saw Doncaster testing the engines for Napier, and by the end of the year a few spare engines were available. 1968 saw the planning for moving Deltic engine overhaul work to Doncaster from Napier, due largely to the continual desire of BR to do as much of its own maintenance work as possible.

The East Coast Main Line regional authorities stressed the importance of the Class 55 fleet — indeed, the whole of the East Coast Main Line service depended on it. A 12-month changeover period from Napier to Doncaster was suggested until an equal work load was obtained, to remain on this basis for another year to enable any problems to be overcome. The regional authorities were not accusing Doncaster of being incapable of the work, but were unwilling to take action which would stop Napier's production line, pointing out that it was imprudent in any case to shed all the load in so short a period as between 1 January and 21 March 1969. Doncaster could have gained useful experience by repairing Class 23 T9-29 Deltic engines, but withdrawals of the class prevented this. Doncaster insisted that it would take over all engine work in March 1969, and the spares were being ordered.

Subsequently, it was decided that Doncaster would repair its first Deltic engine in December 1968, and that apart from this Napier would do all the other engines until 21 March 1969. Thence the work would be shared equally by Napier and Doncaster until Napier had overhauled a sufficient number to enable them to deliver 13 spare overhauled engines from 31 March 1969 onwards.

An analysis of Class 55 failures during 1968 showed that 25% were due to failures of engine components, mainly pistons, liner seals, and liners.

By 1969 Napier was part of EE Diesels Ltd, and it was opined that the firm had been unable to produce repaired engines at a rate to match the engines in service reaching their 5000 hours' service life.

The first Doncaster-repaired engine (Serial No 417) with new pistons was due off test on 2 May 1969, a second engine was being built up, and another was being dismantled for overhaul. There was some disagreement between Napier and Doncaster on the quantity of spares which should be stocked, Doncaster's assessment being less than that of Napier's, stating that the former could cannibalize the 13 spare engines to make up the difference between the assessments. The East Coast Main Line regional authorities stated this was unsatisfactory and the spare engines were not to be dismantled.

By the end of July 1969 four Doncaster-overhauled engines were in service, and the work appears to have proceeded quite well, apart from shortages of some components, until early 1971 when engine deliveries became slower. By July 1971 it was agreed that Doncaster should be supplying at least two overhauled engines per week to maintain the Class 55 fleet in service. Napier/English Electric Diesels (which was by then Paxman Diesels, part of GEC Diesels Ltd) could supply spares for three repaired engines per week, but Doncaster had only ordered spares for one engine per week. At the end of 1971 there was a shortage of engine spares due to Paxman's own sub-contractors concentrating on larger orders for other manufacturers.

In mid-1972 three locomotives were held in Doncaster works because they required five repaired engines which were not available. By September 1972 two locomotives were awaiting engines and only two repaired engines were promised in the near future, but there was a shortage of quillshafts, hub gears and coupling gears, and piston failures were causing extensive secondary damage which was proving expensive to repair.

During the period January to May 1973 ten engines were required to meet scheduled replacements on eight Class 55 locomotives. The only problem was a shortage of main generator armatures which were being refurbished. 1973 passed relatively free of engine shortages, but a shortage of components, notably gears and crankshafts, was reported during October.

1974 was another year in which the repair of

View from above showing power unit installation in one half of the prototype *Deltic* locomotive. (*GEC Traction Ltd*)

engines fell short of the requirements of locomotives due for classified repairs, but by October the position had eased so that there were just enough engines to meet requirements. The position again deteriorated by January 1975 when five locomotives were at Doncaster awaiting engines, where only one engine was available with six others in assembly and on test. There was a shortage of crankcases, 42K liners, idler and exciter drive gears, and cooling fan drives, while industrial action at Paxman's works caused further delays.

June 1975 revealed that there were ten engines to cover two locomotives undergoing classified repairs and three on unclassified repairs. The shortage of spares, notably crankcases, was not likely to be resolved for some five months, and 28 engines would be required during the last 25 weeks of 1975. It was thought that as one locomotive was likely to be in works awaiting engines for the remainder of the year, this locomotive would be the subject of the first general repair, to establish the content of the work required on the body for future general repairs on Class 55. By October both BR and GEC had undertaken the investigation and a general repair proposal was being prepared, but the shortage of engines resulted in classified repairs on some locomotives being postponed until 1976.

By January 1977 it was felt that the position was improving slightly, but by June industrial action at Doncaster, involving a dispute about the

removal of blue asbestos from cab roofs and bulkheads, was threatening availability, with eight locomotives in works. It also appeared that locomotives might have to be taken out of service and stored awaiting repairs if the action continued. There was a shortage of pistons at the time and older types were having to be fitted. By this time of course estimates on the remaining life of Class 55 had made assessments of spares in hand necessary, as it was desirable that large stocks of spares should not be left when the locomotives were withdrawn from service.

During 1977 the 'shopping' periodicity of Class 55 was being re-examined and 55015 was selected to remain in service for two years to see if all locomotives could be given the extended length of time. By early 1978 a shortage of skilled staff at Doncaster works was slowing-down engine work and there were four locomotives in works and another due, all needing engines, while two more on classified repairs had now reached the engine stage. In June 1978 it was reported that out of 20 classified repairs due in 1978 only four had been completed, in the main the low output again being due to industrial action. This unsatisfactory situation caused BR to decide to shop the Class 55 fleet on an ad hoc basis.

Shortages of engine components, gudgeon-pin housings in particular, plus injector nozzles, were preventing engine completion and testing, while the current demand was for five engines each fortnight. The situation was such that locomotive availability for the fleet would be difficult to maintain above 50%. In October 1978 only seven out of the twenty 1978 classified repairs had been

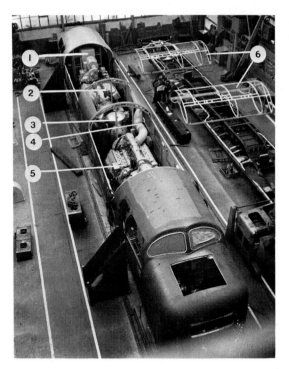

Engines installed in Class 55 during construction at Vulcan Foundry in 1961.

Key:
1. Control cubicle
2. No 2 engine and generator group
3. Steam generator
4. Air intake for scavenge blower
5. No 1 engine and generator group
6. Framework for cooling group under construction

(*GEC Traction Ltd*)

completed. The 18-month shopping periodicity applied on an ad hoc basis was to continue, and it was reported that 55015 had given two years' satisfactory service as part of a special exercise, indicating that an extension beyond 18 months was possible.

In October 1978 there were six locomotives on unclassifieds, each awaiting two engines, one locomotive on unclassified for one engine, four locomotives in service with only one engine in a condition to be used, and one locomotive in works on classified repairs requiring two engines, giving a current requirement of 19 engines. Doncaster had ten engines in progress but only two of these had a promised date of completion. The resultant loss of 12 locomotives was having a very serious effect on East Coast Main Line services.

By late January 1979 there were seven locomotives in works for unclassified repair, each awaiting two engines and two locomotives on classifieds awaiting two engines each, the shortage of gudgeon-pin housings being the main cause, but Paxman was seeking to rectify the situation. June saw little improvement, with six locomotives in works all awaiting two engines each, two of these locomotives, Nos 55001 and 55020, having been there for over a year, in fact since 24 March 1978 and 26 April 1978 respectively. Ten engines were awaiting piston rings and gudgeon-pin housings from Paxman.

The introduction of the High-Speed Inter-City 125 trains in fleet service during 1979 took a heavy load off Class 55, but ad hoc shopping was to continue. By February 1980, following the scrapping of Nos 55001 and 55020, only one locomotive was in works for classified repair, and there were eleven locomotives to shop in 1980. The story since then has been one of better availability, mainly in the 61–72% range.

The termination of the Class 55 spares contract by the BRB Director of Supplies caused BREL Doncaster much concern, especially as in future all orders would have to go through the Director of Supplies to determine if they were essential.

The first instance of piston seizure in the 18-cylinder Deltic engine fitted to Class 55 occurred in March 1962 with locomotive D9017, which was sent to RSH Darlington works for change of engine. The engine was passed to Napier which upon dismantling found that an inlet piston had seized, breaking its connecting rod, after a service life of some 900 hours. The connecting-rod had failed at its big-end, smashing through the crankcase, damaging a crankshaft and other engine components. Failures of connecting-rods had started in 1961 when two varieties of rod were in use in Deltic engines, the unpolished close-forged rod, and the polished close-forged rod. Initially, until metallurgical reports were prepared there was a suspicion that one of the big-end cap bolts had not been tightened or locked properly. The verdict was that the unpolished rod was at fault, so the fully-machined polished rod was adopted. However, it was the end of the year before sufficient rods were available for all engines, and a close watch was kept on the suspect rods already fitted.

In August 1964 it was announced that a MkIV piston with bolted crown of hydural on an aluminium skirt was being fitted to two Deltic engines for trials; if a success, it would replace the MkIIIa pistons during engine overhauls. Both engines were put into D9019 in the autumn of

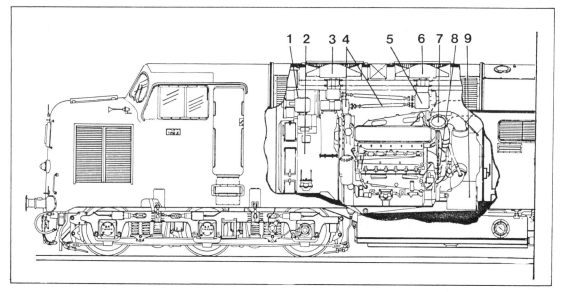

Cut-away side elevation of No 1 end of Class 55
showing No 1 engine and cooling fan arrangement.
Key:
1. Auxiliary generator
2. Main generator
3. Oil radiator fan
4. Take off gear
    to auxiliary
    fan drive gearbox
5. Auxiliary gearbox
6. Coolant radiator fan
7. Scavenge blower
    air intake
8. Scavenge blower
9. Oil reservoir

(*Brian Webb*)

1964. The pistons then in use on the Deltic engines
were the MkIIIa and MkIIIc. The former had
given considerable trouble with loose piston
crowns, these being of screwed-crown type, as was
the IIIc, but in this case the piston was given
improved fitting and the crown additionally
pegged to improve locking. The IIIc piston was
considerably more reliable and was fitted to about
half the engines by March 1965. A MkIIIb piston
had been developed and tested by Napier but it
was not used by BR.

By late 1966 there were five Deltic engines with
MkIV pistons, and these appeared to be
successful. Following a failure in March 1967 at
2130 engine hours, the position changed and all
five engines so fitted were removed by the year end.

The Deltic engine on BR has had a history of
piston problems and these were particularly severe
in late 1966, so much so that their frequency was
affecting the supply of repaired engines to keep
locomotives in service. Engine failures were not
necessarily due to one component failing, and
piston failures were caused by metal fatigue,
gudgeon-pin housing fractures, faulty fuel

injectors, overheating, cylinder liner fractures,
crankshaft problems and others.

It was estimated in late 1968 that some 25% of
Class 55 failures were due to engine component
failures, and it was suggested that the scheduled
Deltic engine life of 5000 hours should be reduced
to 4000 hours to improve reliability. At this time
Napier was having difficulty in producing
sufficient repaired engines to match those in
service reaching their 5000 hours' life, resulting in
some engines exceeding 5000 hours; engines with
insufficient life hours remained to carry the
locomotives to which they were fitted through to
their next classified repairs, an aim which BR tried
to achieve.

The three main engine problems at this time
were pistons, fracturing of liners, and liner seal
failures. So far as pistons were concerned, some
were known to have manufacturing faults and thus
more prone to failure, so only new rather than
reconditioned pistons were to be fitted. Ordering
procedures also delayed piston deliveries. Failure
of pistons continued, and by 1971 pistons were
being ultrasonically tested prior to fitting; every

D9000 in its final guise as 55022 *Royal Scots Grey*, burns off some residual lubricating oil as it opens-up at Meadowbank, Edinburgh, with the 13.25 Edinburgh–London on 3 May 1980. (*Iain M. Flynn*)

rejected piston was an engine failure less, a particularly important step in view of the serious side effects of piston failures.

By this time the Napier Deltic engine production had become part of GEC Diesels Ltd and the work had been moved from Liverpool to the Paxman works at Colchester.

An improved MkIV bolted-crown piston was produced by Paxman for testing in four Deltic engines in 1973, D9005 receiving the first two engines so fitted when it left Doncaster works on 26 January 1973. In the meantime, pending results, a screwed-crown piston with increased thread was to be used from October 1973. These had a higher torsional resistance but could not be supplied in engine sets, so mixed piston types had to be fitted in the engines, taking away much of the hoped-for improvement.

By early 1975 it had become clear that until all the Deltic engines had been fitted with the new MkIV bolted-crown pistons, the problems of detached crowns and piston seizures would continue. It was unfortunate that when BR decided to change to the MkIV piston in August 1974, Paxman was not immediately advised, with the result that some six to seven months' delivery delay occurred. The delay meant that it was necessary to continue to use some of the existing pistons until 1977, leaving engines at risk. The two

points giving cause for concern at this time were the relatively short engine life at which some of the failures occurred, and the fact that when a failure did arise this was sometimes accompanied by the destruction of a crankcase. In the first, every piston was being ultrasonically tested and given other tests so that there was no reason why they should not run for 5000 to 6000 hours without failure. With the latter the delivery of new crankcases was at a lower rate than the equivalent rate of destruction by piston failure. The end-product was loss of Class 55 availability, since locomotives were held in Doncaster works because of the shortage of crankcases.

In 1975 in order to try to anticipate engine failures, particularly piston defects, two aspects were involved, the first being the spectro-graphic analysis of engine lubricating oil. This technique was applied by taking samples of Deltic engine lubricating oil at depots at set engine-hour periods, and these were then sent for analysis at the Doncaster area laboratory. This process at once revealed whether or not a particular engine was in trouble, enabling early action to be taken to prevent piston failure. This technique was not a full precaution, as piston failures arose from other causes not revealed by spectro-graphic analysis. A weekly visual inspection of the engines was a second precaution. This was done by BR locomotive engineers riding on the locomotives to study the engines under load and ascertain which engines were in trouble piston-wise.

Between November 1975 and January 1976

$22\frac{1}{2}$ engine sets of the bolted-crown MkIV piston out of a total of 960 pistons ordered had been delivered to BR by Paxman, the balance being due by early 1977, thus enabling all the Deltic engines to be fitted with them by the end of that year. Piston failures reduced dramatically and by February 1978 the entire engine stock had received new pistons. Although piston failures continue to occur, these are now at an acceptable level, but it took a long time in the life of the engines to reach this stage.

Shortly after the Class 55 entered service in 1961 there began a series of failures due to fractures in the cylinder liners. These liners were of a thin-wall type and had solid lands, the failure rate reaching 25–30% of the liners fitted. The principal causes of liner failures in Deltic engines were quoted in January 1962 as cavitational erosion, which usually originated in the scroll section of the liner, fatigue caused by erosion at the outer edge of the injector adaptor hole, and thermal stressing caused by exhaust gases blowing through defective adaptor seals, originating in the adaptor hole.

On Class 55, liner failures had by this time occurred due to the first and third reasons above. All Class 55 engines had the adaptor seats modified and treated against cavitational erosion and an improved high-pressure sealing washer was fitted to deal with the thermal stressing problem, but Napier emphasised to BR that to give an additional safeguard BR should use glycol (common anti-freeze) coolant treatment in the Deltic engines, this being the most effective cavitation inhibitor on the market.

The water treatment adopted for the Class 55 train-heating steam generators began to attack the steam generator water tanks, which being of aluminium alloy were susceptible to alkaline corrosion. EE stated that the treatment was quite unsuitable, especially in view of the arrangement whereby the Deltic engine cooling system could be topped-up from the steam generator water supply. The possibility of corrosion of alloy engine components, and some liner failures were put down to this cause.

EE advised BR to abandon steam generator water treatment, pointing out that the prototype locomotive had run 433,000 miles without special water treatment for it. In practice the prototype *Deltic* picked up treated water so that in fact some degree of treatment of the steam generator water was applied. However, BR chose to continue to treat the steam generator water, in its opinion to save retubing them every six months.

During 1962–3 liner troubles continued and the use of unsuitable engine coolant additives was blamed for liner erosion, shortage of spares making it difficult to keep one spare engine in stock. Thirty Deltic engines were fitted with reconditioned liners by mid-1963, but there were many failures during the summer of 1963, so firmer action was required.

Napier introduced a strengthened liner which was fitted progressively, so that the end of 1964 saw all the liners replaced. The main differences between the two types of liner were that the strengthened one had approximately 0.0625in increased radial wall thickness in the combustion area, increased cooling lands, and spirally-rolled liner tube forgings were used instead of axially-rolled tubes to increase strength in relation to the grain-flow of the metal. The latter precaution proved of little benefit and both types of forgings were generally used according to supply. Failure rate was progressively reduced to approximately 5–10%, but work continued to try to establish the basic cause of the fractures.

It was found that the fracturing was due to erosion fatigue originating in the area of the injector and blanking holes. To combat this a number of plating processes such as tin, copper, 22-carat gold, cadmium, together with various types of fillers, were tried on the adaptor holes. The cooling water guide grooves round the combustion area of the liner were changed from deep helical grooves to small helical projections, and modification of the injector blank adaptor holes created a non-threaded portion in the area where the erosion fatigue fracturing was found to originate, namely in the thread of the holes. A modification introduced in 1966 was the progressive replacement of the solid land liners with spring land liners. This was done to reduce fretting between the liner lands and the cylinder block bores, but the liner problems were by no means solved.

During the changeover in the repair of Deltic engines from Napier to BR Doncaster works – a gradual process spread between April and September 1969 – some misgivings about the ability of Doncaster to carry out engine repair work to the highly experienced and specialised standards of Napier was expressed by BR regional authorities, even though a training programme for BR personnel had been successfully completed at Napier's works.

Unfortunately, some of the Napier engine component records were insufficient to provide comparative figures for their period of engine maintenance, and no record of individual liner history was available, so it was not known whether the life of liners after Doncaster took over was increasing or decreasing.

The practice for reclaiming cylinder liners was to send the liners to Napier which achieved a high repair standard, but when the Deltic engine work was moved to Colchester the standard was unintentionally reduced. A process of inspection of the liners was initiated at Doncaster to improve the position and ensure that no suspect liners were fitted in repaired engines. Lack of experience and expertise at Paxman's Colchester works was probably part of the problem. A shortage of liners was the result. To overcome the shortage of liners and in order to keep Class 55 in service, a supply of a new type of liner hitherto not used by BR was obtained. This was the 42K liner and was currently in production by Paxman for other Deltic engine customers. The 42K liner was used initially as a stopgap but its use necessitated, as with the strengthened standard liners, reboring of the cylinder blocks to cope with their oversize. Reboring meant that restoration of the blocks to take other liners was not easily possible, so BR decided on a campaign change to 42K liners from September 1971.

During the period October 1970 to May 1971 the Deltic engine failure rate was catastrophic, with a peak of 31 engines out of the 57 engines for the whole fleet under repair. Not all of these failures were due to the liners, but a large proportion was. The situation was aggravated by shortages of engine components due in part to insufficient stocks of spares and delays in ordering replacement stocks, resulting in slow delivery from Paxmans, and the inability of Doncaster works to supply enough repaired engines at the right time.

During 1971 Paxman put in hand experimental work in building-up by welding the cylinder block lands, with the aim of being able to rebore these to accept standard liners.

The 42K liner was fitted to three Deltic engines by February 1972 and these were under careful observation. Paxman had not claimed any special advantage for the 42K liner, from a mechanical reliability standpoint, over the liner currently in use by BR. Some delay in fitting 42K liners was caused by Doncaster deciding to select only the worst cylinder blocks for reboring, rather than any block which came to hand.

Deltic engine problems were in part due to lack of foresight. Napier practice when overhauling the engines had been to use standard liners with various levels of salvage and the occasional use of new liners having +0.030in and +0.060in oversizes. This technique was known to BR at the time Doncaster took-over the engines, but neither Napier nor BR appeared to realise that the use of standard oversize liners was increasing, hence no provision was made for the production or ordering of such liners. With Napier mainly producing 42K liners for its own use, Doncaster was managing on salvage limits applied to existing standard liners, but did order 12 sets of non-oversize liners just in case.

The steady increase in numbers of cylinder blocks with larger than standard bores was finally realised in early 1971, by which time 42K liners were the only ones available in quantity from Paxman for some months, and later that year a significant number of blocks ready for reboring were too worn to take even 42K liners without reclaiming and remachining. It was expected at this time that up to fifteen months would elapse before Deltic engine life could be raised to 5000 hours again. In June 1972 the average time in service for a Deltic engine was put at 2609 hours, an improvement of 765 hours on previous figures.

In September 1972 there were eight sets of 42K liners in service and no failures had been reported. Replacement of solid land liners by spring land liners had progressed so that about 60% of engines now had these.

Reclamation of cylinder blocks by Paxman was possible at a much lower cost than purchasing new ones and it was suggested that a specialised cylinder block welding machine, capable of doing all six bores in a block at once, should be purchased by BR. This would be used to prepare the blocks for the 42K liners which were only 0.010in greater in diameter than the standard liners. The purchase of a machine was agreed, and trial work started in 1972 at Colchester. In the meantime BR borrowed six new cylinder blocks from Paxman which was necessary, said BR, due to the inability of Paxman to supply a specific type of cylinder liner to suit BR-owned blocks. BR was using in 1972 both standard and 42K liners, the former used until the blocks became too worn to take them and then rebored to a larger size to accept the 42K liner. In October 1972 Paxman suggested that it could now supply reclaimed and

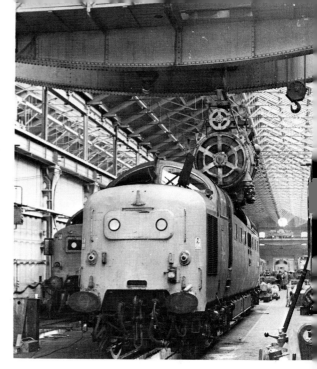

55003 *Meld* in Doncaster works for engine changing on 14 February 1979. (*Roger Newling-Goode*)

rebored cylinder blocks to take standard liners at a bulk price of £443 each, compared with the cost of £2200 for a new block.

Troubles with erosion fatigue between the injector adaptor and the hole in the liner continued, due in part to deterioration of the lead-based sealing compound, usually following the changing of injectors at depots, which disturbed the adaptor. To avoid this, injector changing was recommended to be transferred to Doncaster works.

In 1971 the failure of liner seals made of pure rubber, rubber and nitrile, and nitrile, was put down to the damaging effect of poor fits of solid land liners in worn cylinder block bores, but spring land liners with nitrile seals even in worn bores were marginally more reliable. The mixing of solid and spring land liners in one engine was not conducive to reliability and it was suggested in October that the practice should cease, although supplies of liners did not always permit this to be done.

Spring land liners and nitrile seals were used when possible and by May 1973 there had been a marked reduction in liner seal failures, only two being reported in a 17-week period; both of these were solid land liners with natural rubber seals. In January 1974 there had been no liner seal failures for 16 weeks, due mainly to the elimination of natural rubber seals and solid land liners, nor have any further failures been reported since 1974.

All types of liners – solid land, spring land, and 42K – were still fracturing, there being 12 in one 54-week period, all due to injector adaptor hole erosion. Possible additional causes, such as increases in load factors due to the locomotives' higher speed operation for longer periods of time, engines operating at full power for longer periods of time, and the fitting of electric train heating, were considered. Also, the continued changing of injectors at depots was thought to be a possible cause in early 1974, but it was hoped that this would cease when Doncaster works took on injector changing. However, depots still perform this task.

Over the period since 1974 the progressive fitting of 42K liners in the reclaimed and remachined cylinder blocks, together with the use of spring lands and elimination of adaptor hole erosion, has reduced liner failures to an acceptable level, which continued to be so in 1980.

Figures available concerning liner failures for 1970–3 are:

Year	Failures due to fractured liners	Class 55 fleet engine hours	Fleet mileage
1970	15	164,687	3,534,508
1971	15	139,066	2,943,769
1972	10	167,769	3,454,835
1973	12	178,564	3,711,531

Piston failures in which the connecting-rod fractured the crankcase arose to serious proportions in 1978. The cause was thought likely to be one of three faults, circlip failures, insufficient interference fit between gudgeon-pin housing and piston body for service conditions, or disintegration of the gudgeon-pin housing bushes, and discussions with Paxman were held to try to solve the problem.

As a precautionary measure, from June 1978 all MkIV pistons, including latest type gudgeon-pin housing, had to be inspected after 3000 hours' service life; the maximum life of the gudgeon-pin housing bushes was 5000 hours. Withdrawal of locomotives with housings which had reached or passed 3000 hours, or those in the region of 5000 hours, was authorised, but if at 2000 hours the housings were found to be in good condition, a further 2000 hours' service would be permitted. Paxman decided to try alternative materials for gudgeon-pin housing bushes, increase the fit between piston and housing, and fit a heavier circlip than that currently used. The resultant shortage of MkIV piston components made it necessary to revert to fitting MkIII pistons in some overhauled engines, a retrograde but unavoidable step made worse by the necessity to examine these engines every 2000 hours. The purchase of further new crankcases was authorised, which it was hoped would be sufficient to cover the remaining life of the locomotives.

In consequence of the shortage of engine spares – notably gudgeon-pin housings – it was decided in January 1979 to reduce Class 55 fleet availability to 50% from 64%, the average for the previous six weeks being 52%. Further deterioration for the same reasons reduced availability to 42% in the six weeks ending 28 April 1979, 343 locomotive-days being lost. By the end of 1979 availability had risen to 68.1%, so the 1980 target for the fleet was set at 55%.

The actual engine-hour target of 6000 hours between overhaul has aroused much argument, and although 5000 hours was the norm, some engines have exceeded 6000 hours, and more recently with the pressure off the locomotives, over 7000 hours and 7500 engine hours have been achieved. It was without doubt the controlling influence of the components and the length of time to remedy their faults which inhibited the Deltic engine from reaching its sought-after service hours target.

In the early days radiator elements were damaged because no anti-freeze was used in the system; the resulting freezing distorted the radiators, which when repaired with a 2-pack epoxy material, greatly reduced the radiators' cooling surface area. The differing opinions as to the correct type of Deltic engine coolant treatment during 1962 resulted in some engine damage. BR wished to use the sodium benzoate or their standard chromate treatment, but Napier recommended ethylene glycol which was more suitable for engines incorporating lightweight alloys, and EE supported this view regardless of cost. Even J. F. Harrison and E. S. Cox differed on the coolant to be used, only the former supporting Napier and EE. During October 1962 a change to ethylene glycol was made, and engine erosion problems eased.

Class 55 locomotives started to suffer coolant radiator problems during 1973 when a number of locomotives failed with high water temperatures. Investigation revealed some locomotives fitted with flexible hoses of incorrect specification and on others that radiators required removal for flushing-out and exterior high-pressure cleaning, while in some instances the high water temperature warning switches were incorrectly set.

The age and condition of the radiators resulted in new ones being fitted during 1975 as the original ones failed their water flow tests due to the build up of scale etc. High water temperatures continued but always with the older radiators, which in some cases was due to radiators having had extensive repairs carried out by Doncaster works in order to rehabilitate scrapped ones to a 'passable' condition during 1975–6. Eventually the situation eased and failures because of this were finally overcome by the delivery of new radiators.

SUMMARY OF CLASS 55 ENGINE FAILURES 1973–9 GIVING NUMBER OF CASES

Failure	1973	1974	1975	1976	1977	1978	1979
Crankcases						1	
Fractured liners	10	14	13	9	10	10	13
Liner seals	15		1				
Pistons	8	16	21	25	15	5	2
Quillshafts	9	9	3	4	7	5	3
Damper					3		
Damper bolts		7	4	5		3	
Connecting-rod							1
Phasing case – roller bearings				2	1		2
Main generator – drive shaft					4	1	4
Scavenge-blower Impeller						1	1
Hub gear							1
Exciter gear							1
Gudgeon-pin housing							1

CHAPTER 8

CLASS 55 DELTIC SERVICE PROBLEMS

A long-standing problem considered of prime importance by Class 55 locomotive crews was the notoriously draughty cabs in these locomotives. This was noted immediately the locomotives entered service, and was due to the indifferent fitting of the sliding cabside doors. Attention to door fittings and latches certainly improved the condition, but complaints continued periodically until 1971 when they became serious once again. This time the cabside windows were given modified catches and new draught strips, rollers, while front and back draught screens were fitted to the doors, with some improvement. Tests on the problem in 1974 revealed that draught from the doors was caused partly by the flexing of the locomotive body shell and by air being drawn by the nose-mounted traction motor blower under the driver's control panel. The sound-proofing curtain did not stop draughts.

In January 1976 a modification was introduced to provide the traction motor blower with its air via an underfloor air duct, thus removing the sucking of air through gaps in the cab-to-nose-compartment bulkhead. Modification proved a prolonged process and was considered to be only partly successful; by early 1980 five locomotives remained to be fitted.

Soon after the first few Class 55s had entered service in 1961, a more serious problem began, a spate of serious bogie defects which arose simultaneously with identical defects on the new EE Class 37 locomotives which had the same bogie design.

The first problem was with the rubbing plates for the transom of the bogie bolster, which were becoming loose, quickly followed by fractures in the vicinity of the traction motor nose suspension brackets on the bogie transom. Remedial work was put in hand by EE in March 1961, consisting of fixing the rubbing plates to the bogie frame by welding, and fitting a stiffening plate to the bottom flanges of the transom of the bogies of the locomotives already in service to avoid unduly long periods out of traffic. The bogies for locomotives still under construction at VF were given a revised profile of bottom flange plate with

$\frac{5}{8}$in thickness instead of $\frac{1}{2}$in.

EE put in hand a series of tests involving the Whetstone Metallurgical laboratories, which would be fully comprehensive but require some time to complete, promising a full report on their findings.

The first Class 55 delivered with the above modifications was D9005 on 18 May, and a small float of modified bogies was built up to meet requirements as they arose. The most unfortunate outcome of the bogie situation was the delay in introducing Class 55 into full-scale service and hence the delaying of the long awaited timetable improvements. Locomotives D9000–3 were to be provided with new bogies, as they were available, during the locomotives' 6-monthly bogie change periods. Dynamic strain gauge tests of the bogies was instigated on D9009, which was instrumented by EE Whetstone before leaving VF. Initially between 17 July and 20 July 1961 static bogie-loading tests to check the effect of the weight of the superstructure on the bogies were conducted with both engines running on full power and with the locomotive stationary. These were followed by running tests between King's Cross and Doncaster on 22 August.

By this time BR was concerned about three bogie defects:

1. Breakage of bogie anchor brackets on the transom.
2. Loosening and heavy wear in traction motor nose suspension, and also on the transoms.
3. Fractures on the bogie frame inner and outer member adjacent to the brake hanger brackets.

Preventive 'first aid' modifications were made to the sound bogie headstocks, the fractured headstocks requiring rather that the locomotives be withdrawn temporarily from service for remedial work by EE at either RSH or VF.

The remedial work, and orders not to use Class 55 on high-speed workings, considerably upset regional driver training schedules, and management was concerned about this in view of the plans for the locomotives in the coming

55002 *The King's Own Yorkshire Light Infantry* casts a giant shadow approaching Plawsworth at 08.03 on 2 September 1978, with a rather late up Anglo-Scottish sleeper loaded to 16 vehicles, for which Deltic power and steam-heating capacity was a firm favourite. (*Brian Webb*)

1961–2 winter timetables. J. F. Harrison for the BTC suggested a campaign bogie change and pointed out that it was imperative that eleven locomotives were available for the new timetable in September. Accordingly, D9000/2/8/10 received new bogies in August at RSH, and D9005–7/9 in August–September at VF. It was planned that all would be done by 8 September so that there would be thirteen Class 55 locomotives available for the new timetable on 11 September.

During 1962, with all the troubles experienced

The popularity of Class 55 for excusions and special train duties grew during the middle to late 1970s. On 23 July 1978 a Sheffield 'Merrymaker' on its homeward-bound run traverses the Settle & Carlisle line and rouses the area from its Sunday rest by having 55003 *Meld* at its head. (*Brian Webb*)

with Class 55 and the ever-growing Class 37 fleet, thought had been given to replacing the troublesome fabricated bogie frames with cast-steel, at least on further locomotives, and a number of firms at home and overseas were asked to quote for bogie frames in batches of 50, 100 and 200.

In December 1962 D9007/13 were found to have hair-line fractures on their bogies (in spite of their having strengthened headstocks) at the end of the strengthening plate. It was decided that this could be prevented from recurring by extending the weld beyond the strengthening plate and sealing it at the end of the parent material. The defect was not considered serious.

A series of brake gear problems occurred during 1962, being a continuation of earlier troubles when several Class 55 bogie brake tie-rods were found to be out of true in relation to the tyre, and examination of other tie-rods confirmed this, and that the rods were not centrally located. Brake problems continued in 1963, when it was decided

to replace ferobestos pads forming the rubbing surfaces of the inner brake block carrier side stops with welded on steel pads.

BR Research Department tests on unmodified Class 37 bogies showed that the section of transom investigated was in fact bending in both the horizontal and vertical planes, suggesting that the modifications by EE were not effective in reducing stresses by a sufficient amount. Early in 1964 a serious failure of a bogie headstock on D9008 again emphasised the weaknesses of the fabricated bogie when fitted to Class 55 engaged on intensive high-speed work. Class 37 was not so susceptible, and it was noted that on locomotives recently delivered by EE, current Class 37 bogies had more robust headstocks. It was decided to make four such headstocks at BR Doncaster for trial use.

During late 1964 bogie fatigue fractures across the side bearer were found, and it was decided to amend those bogies not affected by modifying the gusset, but fractured bogies were to have the gusset removed and an additional plate fitted. By this time the incidence of Class 55 bogie fractures, and to a lesser degree on Class 37, revived the idea of producing an entirely new bogie design for Class 55; indeed the new EE cast-steel bogie fitted to later examples of Class 37. The idea was followed-through quickly so that by mid-January 1965 arrangements were made between EE and BR to replace Class 55 bogies with cast-steel ones, using existing wheels, axles, axleboxes etc. from the fabricated frames, which in turn would be rectified for use on Class 37 locomotives.

On 22 February 1965 twenty-two Class 55 and forty-two Class 37 retained original fabricated bogies, and seventy-seven Class 37 had bogies with strengthened side frame fabricated bogies; 130 Class 37 had improved fabricated bogies, and sixty in course of delivery had cast steel bogies.

As the Class 55 bogie change was now urgent, it was agreed to take ten cast-steel bogies from the current Class 37 deliveries and fit modified fabricated bogies instead, the remaining twelve sets being produced especially for Class 55. A campaign bogie change was planned, commencing in May 1965, using individually selected bogie frames, with the following programme:

Month	No of bogies
May	2
June	8
July	10

August	8
September	8
October	10
November	2

By mid-October fifteen locomotives had been done but by the end of November only D9010 remained with fabricated bogies. This virtually ended the Class 55 bogie problems, although the cast-steel frames still give periodical troubles, and bogie swing link fractures at a point about 4in below the pivot pin hole were found on Classes 37 and 55 during 1974, also on bogie swing link pins and bushes in mid 1975, which required revision of materials.

The saga of the train-heating steam generator of Class 55 could fill its own book, together with the decision to fit the Spanner MkII steam generator, mentioned in Chapter 4. It was BR which made the final decision on which make should be fitted. As it turned out, the steam generator brought a plague of troubles to Class 55, as did other types in other BR classes.

During the first half of 1961 the suction-feed water pipe from the water tank to the steam generator had to be lengthened to avoid water shortages or starvation while the tank was still one-third full, or due to surging of the last 50 to 100 gallons, resulting in the pipe drawing air and the shutting-down of the steam generator.

From the start the steam generator did not operate well with No 2 cab leading. This was opined to be due to the relative positions of the steam generator exhaust outlet and the engine exhaust outlet on the 'B' side of the roof. The air flow over the roof with No 1 cab leading assisted steam generator draughting by creating a partial vacuum above the steam generator exhaust outlet, but No 2 end leading created back-pressure causing intermittent steam generator operation. The prototype *Deltic* had a centre-roof steam generator exhaust, but Class 55 an off-centre outlet. Changing the position of the outlet to the roof centre-line was suggested, but BR objected on clearance and electrification grounds. A further scheme involving the release of the exhaust through the locomotive side was rejected due to lack of space. In spite of BR, EE fitted D9006 with a centre roof outlet in June 1961.

As Class 55 deliveries progressed, steam generator troubles increased, so that in one week of August 1961, one locomotive had failed each night on overnight sleeping trains due to this cause. BR was becoming very apprehensive of what the

The collapse of Penmanshiel tunnel during 1979 resulted in a few Anglo-Scottish workings running via Carlisle. The only regular daytime Deltic diagram was the 05.50 King's Cross–Aberdeen. Here 55022 *Royal Scots Grey* is in charge, appearing to be almost wading through the lush lineside vegetation near Great Corby on the Newcastle–Carlisle line on 19 June 1979. (*Brian Webb*)

coming winter would bring with steam heating in use day and night. EE staff began to accompany overnight trains in late August, starting with The Aberdonian on 24 August, hauled by locomotive D9010. A number of points affecting steam generator performance were noted but it was not possible to decide if the roof exhaust theory worked in practice, especially since runs with the modified D9006 produced identical results to the unmodified locomotives! Spanner, the makers of the generator, insisted that the exhaust problem

Another Penmanshiel diversion, the return working for the locomotive off the 05.50 from King's Cross, the 18.25 Edinburgh–King's Cross with 55006 *The Fife & Forfar Yeomanry* glinting in the low evening sunlight from the Solway Firth as it hums southwards considerably ahead of schedule under the West Coast Main Line wires near Gretna, on 28 June 1979. (*Brian Webb*)

must be dealt with and EE agreed to fit one of the locomotives still being built at VF, but BR again refused the steam generator exhaust in the centre line of roof.

EE suggested splitting the exhaust to two roof outlets, one on 'A' and one on 'B' side of the locomotive roof. BR gave EE authority to fit D9019 and four other locomotives with the EE proposal in October 1961, that is the split or bifurcated exhaust stack, initial observations with D9019 appearing to be satisfactory.

Spanner was still blaming the exhaust system for the steam generator troubles in 1962, EE opining that it was shortage of combustion air which was the real culprit. On D9019 the bifurcated stack gave equal exhaust conditions regardless of direction of running, so EE said that any future trouble on this locomotive could not be levelled at the exhaust, but at the generator itself. D9019 also had various other steam generator modifications done at the same time.

EE staff riding D9019 in January 1962 on Anglo-Scottish workings observed that on fifteen journeys with this and other locomotives the steam generator could not produce the specified 2000lb/hr when called to do so, due probably to

loss of efficiency since new, through sooting of tubes and scaling of tubes. Modifications to the flue and oil-burner gun gave more stable combustion.

J. F. Harrison was of the opinion that more air was required, supplied from a separate source independent of the engine room. In his opinion steam generator blowouts were caused by the lack of air when the Deltic engines were accelerating to full power, and he asked EE to design and fit a steam generator air duct. EE pointed out that in fact the engines drew their air from outside the locomotive, not the engine room. The ducting of steam generator air was rejected because aerodynamic conditions could extract air rather than add it, and the ingress of water when picking-up from troughs at speed was a further danger. The question of air supply persisted and tests on D9019, with bodyside windows open and partly open, and fitted with metal grilles, were undertaken to examine the theory.

In April 1962 EE reported the principal steam generator troubles as bad combustion, blowbacks, lack of steam, lockouts, poor adjustment, and equipment failures. These were due to unsatisfactory flue arrangements, lack of knowledge by Spanner of the conditions in which its steam generator was to operate, poor design of some auxiliaries, and poor and lack of adequate maintenance by BR, due largely to the inexperience of staff.

Modifications in hand and completed, plus adequate training of BR staff, would probably solve most of the steam generator problems, but EE again said that the output would remain insufficient to heat a 15-coach train with a train-line steam pressure of 60lb/sq in.

J. F. Harrison complained that between 12 February and 2 April 1962 there had been 38 failures due to the steam generators on 10 locomotives having bifurcated stacks — 13 electrical, 16 mechanical, and 9 cause unknown. EE Traction Division's London office was demanding positive action, but the EE staff were working full time on the steam generator, and modifications were being done as locomotives and materials were available. Poor maintenance by BR and incorrect water treatment were still being blamed by EE for many of the problems. Work with D9019, on which EE staff had ridden many thousands of miles, continued, but even though stack modifications had resulted in uniform air pressures in both directions of running, Nu-way burners had given better combustion, and

experiments with bodyside window air intakes etc. had taken place, EE was satisfied that poor combustion was not due to shortage of air. Blowbacks of unburnt gases in the steam generator firebox due to delayed fuel ignition caused by faulty ignition electrode setting required to be overcome. Tube-cleaning was inadequate, resulting in soot collecting unburnt fuel, giving-off combustible vapours after steam generator shut-down, subsequently igniting when it came on again, also caused blowbacks. On cases where the locomotives had to be taken off due to inability to heat the trains, it was usually due to falls in steam generator efficiency caused by scaling-up of tubes and inadequate water treatment.

By mid-May 1962 seventeen locomotives had bifurcated stacks, the modification being done at RSH, Finsbury Park, and Haymarket. The opinion of Esso on the steam generators was sought by the BTC, and Esso, EE and BR took part in instrumented tests — both static and running — during October 1962. The findings showed for the first time that running with bodyside windows closed, shortage of air caused poor combustion; the air/fuel mixture was very critical, and this should be constant at all engine speeds; the heat content of the steam was low and was consistent with a large carry-over of water, causing the train pipes to fill with water and thus have less steam capacity; steam leaks in the trains due to faulty connecting hoses between carriages were more serious than had been thought.

The recommendations were as follows. Firstly, to provide more air by running with bodyside windows open. Since this was not desirable due to the effect of rain and dirt on other engine room equipment, a separate air supply to the steam generator was suggested, possibly by ducting the fan inlet to the atmosphere to provide a stable air supply free from the fluctuations caused by stations, tunnels, passing trains, and speed of the locomotive. Another idea was to control the steam generator fuel supply to suit prevailing air conditions, the engine speed governor controlling the steam generator fuel rate, so that as locomotive engines speed-up, the fuel rate slowed, along with the reduction of combustion air. Tests revealed that the dryness of the steam could be improved by reducing the amount of water in the generator, to leave more steam space.

EE was authorised by BR to provide a roof duct, and designed one for roof mounting which with difficulty was fitted to D9015 during January

A common problem with main line diesel locomotives – the malfunctioning of the steam train-heating equipment – Class 55 being no exception. Two comparative views inside the body of the prototype *Deltic* with its Stone-Vapor steam generator (*left*); and a Class 55 (*right*) with a Spanner MkII steam generator, both shots taken prior to fitting the power units. (*GEC Traction Ltd*)

1963, initial running observations indicating that the steam generator operated well enough but that the air duct appeared to impede air flow! In February 1963 D9015 failed at King's Cross with blocked steam generator tubes which had had constant attention since the roof duct was fitted. It was now said that the roof duct was actually drawing in the generator's own exhaust, and Finsbury Park staff wanted to take out the duct. EE wanted to remove the duct, too, so when BR wanted to fit a duct to D9018, the firm suggested BR could save money if it used the one from D9015. The duct was taken out and the generator again took air from the engine room, operating without incident. EE was then asked to prepare an underfloor air duct and also a duct using air from the traction motor blowers.

The following figures give some idea of the magnitude of train-heating steam generator failures on Class 55 during the period September 1962 to February 1963:

Period	10.9.62–17.11.62	17.12.62–23.2.63
ER locomotives	9	16
NER locomotives	13	19
ScR locomotives	21	27
	43	62

These figures contained 68% and 72% of failures due to train-heating steam generators respectively.

The steam generator modification programme overlapped on to the 1963 summer timetable – normally inviolate so far as Class 55 repairs were concerned – and in view of this EE agreed to transfer its prototype 2700hp locomotive DP2 from the LMR to the ER to help out.

Trials with alternative burners in the Spanner MkII units eventually resulted in the adoption of the Nu-way burner in place of the Supreme burner from 1965, and combustion problems, although still very much to the fore, diminished considerably. D9009 was the first locomotive fitted.

During the 1970s, as BR expertise and experience with the equipment increased, steam generator troubles were more associated with their age, and gradual scrapping reduced the stock of Spanner MkII units to 23 for 22 locomotives by mid-1975. Ideas to use Spanner MkIIIb units from Class 47 did not materialise, and in spite of the electric train heating conversion of two trains of East Coast sleeping cars, the Class 55 was still steam-heating sleepers in 1980.

In April 1963 arrangements were made to fit an EE-built Clayton steam generator, then on test at VF, in D9008 which on 18 April had entered Doncaster works for major overhaul. EE planned the alterations to D9008 and trained staff for maintenance, the locomotive returning to service on 7 May. Staff unfamiliarity caused troubles such as water starvation due to blocked filters, controls incorrectly set up, heating coils sooted-up, and failure to attend to its special water treatment, until in 1964 it was brought into line in that respect with the rest of the fleet.

On a King's Cross–Edinburgh test with a sleeping car train in May 1964 the Clayton operated satisfactorily with various bodyside windows open or closed, and with ducted in air, combustion being good. The steam generator was able to produce 2200lb of steam per hour. Its non-standard fittings made the locomotive an 'odd man out' and even by June it was being suggested for refitting with its Spanner steam generator. It was stated that the Clayton unit had failed eight times between October 1963 and April 1964, while an average of only 5.2 Spanner steam generators had failed in the same period. Plans to refit the Spanner steam generator at D9008's 6-monthly bogie change due in November 1964 were cancelled owing to the extra time the locomotive would have to remain in works. In fact, the Clayton unit was to remain until May 1965.

By that time the position had been reversed and the other 21 Class 55s were suffering more troubles with their Spanner units and the suggestion was made that all these should now be made standard with D9008! Unfortunately, D9008 was in Doncaster works at the time and work removing the Clayton steam generator and its fittings had progressed to the point where some Spanner fittings had been refitted – past the point of no return!

Steam generator performance statistics for Class 55 at May 1965 were:

Type of steam generator	Number of locomotives fitted	Number of casualties	Number of failures per locomotive
Clayton RO 2500 MkII	1	12	12
Spanner MkII with Supreme burner	19	104	8
Spanner MkII with Nu-way burner	1	4	4

The steam generator of D9008 was officially changed on 29 May 1965, so ending EE hopes of a second chance to fit its own unit to Class 55.

During delivery of the locomotives in 1961, BR informed EE that it wished the warning horns to be mounted on the cab roof rather than under the bufferbeam, EE pointing out that this had been the intention until the BR design panel objected to this on aesthetic grounds. EE said it could fit the last few locomotives, D9019–21, before they left VF, and that their prototype locomotive DP2 would be so fitted. Doubts about the audibility of the horns had resulted in EE wishing to fit the Desilux horn made by C. V. Desiderio in London but, the BR-approved horn made by Trico-Folbirth was in fact fitted. The horns proved neither robust enough nor reliable on Class 55 and 20 had failed by November 1962, due in part to incorrect assembly. The roof mounting of the horns on D9019–21 proved successful and it was recommended in late 1962 that all Class 55 be so fitted.

Further doubts about the efficiency of the Class 55 warning horns resulted in the testing of a number of types of horns during the 1964–7 period in different positions on the locomotives. The original position for the Class 55 horns was beneath the bufferbeams which made the horns less audible and subjected them to much punishment from water, dirt, oil and flying ballast. The new horns were tested in the standard Class 55 roof position, on the top of the nose in front of the cab windows, and with the horns fitted inside the nose with apertures at each side of the nose-front. In mid-1967 tests between Arlesey and Great Ponton revealed that horns on the nose in front of the cab windows was best, although not as good as hoped for, and this fitting was adopted for the whole class. Horns were damaged in washing plants and had their trumpets knocked off; the horns are now suitably stayed to prevent this. The horns chosen and still retained are the Westinghouse 'Pneuphonic'.

The first firm proposals for the conversion of Class 55 to electric train heating (ETH) came from BRB, and EE was asked to consider the matter in August 1965. J. F. Harrison for BRB suggested that the existing auxiliary generator could be replaced by a 3-phase alternator with 110V and 880V windings for supplying auxiliaries and ETH respectively, both outputs being rectified. They were to be self-excited with initial build-up taken from the locomotive battery, and to incorporate controls which provided a constant voltage over the whole of the diesel engine speed range.

EE had some experience of supplying ETH for BR, in that the SR diesel-electric multiple units had been thus fitted since 1956. Class 40 D255 had undergone ETH trials in 1960 by tapping the main generator, and various proposals had been put forward concerning Classes 37 and 40 during 1964, some involving engine upratings to provide for the ETH load. No scheme had been put forward for Class 55.

Fitting ETH to Class 55 was not an easy task for a number of reasons:

1. The main generators were connected in series, each machine having a voltage of 900, so that any ETH scheme would have to work from one power unit only.
2. The high power of Class 55 meant that on light trains on slower timings the locomotives ran on part power, thus reducing ETH output.
3. BRB wanted ETH outputs of 250kW for a 15-coach train at 800V. Class 55 locomotives could not do this.
4. Directly-driven ETH generators could not be mounted on the Class 55 main generator as it had no shaft extension, nor was there space at the generator end.
5. Removal of the Spanner steam generator would not provide room for a separate diesel-generator set of required output. This would, if feasible, be a costly job, in view of control gear required.

By September 1965 EE was able to offer a scheme to BRB involving both engines running, but only one taking the load up to its maximum output. The engine remained on maximum output, with the second engine building-up, and both finally providing full output, and full load, the engines being interchangeable. Some control modifications were necessary for this scheme.

By mid 1966 the matter was still under discussion and BRB was not prepared to consider the main generator scheme. BRB said the provision of engine-driven alternators, involving a long cardan shaft back over the top of the engines, was possible, as was modification of the main generator end housings to take a short alternator of 150kW rating. If EE could not provide the solution, BRB would go elsewhere. EE was still convinced that its scheme of taking direct current for ETH from the main generators was best, and finally took mock-ups of their equipment to Doncaster works in July to see if it would fit a Class 55. The result? The BRB agreed to the fitting of one locomotive in late 1966, D9007 being chosen.

During extensive tests in January 1967 it was found that the locomotive could supply adequate ETH and maintain schedules, but the level of ETH was not adequate with a light train and the locomotive at reduced engine power. Further modifications to D9007 were made. BR would not permit removal of the train-heating steam generator as Class 55 duties required them to provide both forms of heating.

The 15–16 January 1967 tests between King's Cross and Newcastle showed that the increased generator loading had little effect on locomotive performance and that temperatures in the coaches reached the acceptable 62–65°F after $1\frac{1}{2}$ to 2 hours, and levelled-off to 62–71°F after $2\frac{1}{2}$ to 3 hours. Doubts about the adequacy of the ETH equipment when used with slower and heavier trains was expressed.

The expected introduction of new 'ETH-only' coaching stock on the East Coast Main Line in September 1970 meant that plans had to be made with some urgency for fitting the Class 55 fleet. Economically it was wisest to fit ETH during intermediate repairs, but as this occurred at 15-month intervals it meant starting conversion in June 1969. This being impossible, it would be necessary to modify some locomotives during light repairs, thus extending the time in works with a loss of availability, but delaying the start of the programme until early 1970. For various reasons the first locomotive was not scheduled for conversion until April 1970.

When D9007 was first fitted during 1966, it could only supply ETH from its No 1 main generator, but on the fleet conversion it was an entirely different operation, as follows:

1. Both engines must be operational to supply ETH, ie to complete the circuit.
2. With the power handle closed, both engines running at idling speed, and the ETH switched on, both generators are fully excited and connected in series to produce 850V.
3. Opening of the power handle switches-off ETH and a time delay relay of three seconds' duration prevents power for traction being applied, whilst the ETH contractors automatically switch-over to take power from the generator at the leading end of the locomotive, and then supply traction and ETH power simultaneously. Traction power is not being robbed by the train's ETH system during starting, as the ETH contractors do not close until a minimum of 600V is being supplied. The normal voltage

required to move a locomotive and train away from rest is 400V.

4. When the power handle is closed the circuits revert to the condition in 2 above after a delay of ten seconds, the delay being to prevent unnecessary switching, should the driver shut off power momentarily for a signal etc.

Although ETH was supplied by one generator – always the generator at the leading end of the locomotive – both generators were ETH-fitted but only one was used at any one time. However, when the train was standing and supplying ETH as in stations, or with engine power shut off – coasting at speed – the engines were idling. In these instances both generators supplied ETH in series at a fixed 850V.

Locomotives D9021 and D9009 were fitted with ETH on 19 September and 17 October 1970 respectively, being subject to some delay due to other repair work requirements on them. By 25 February 1971 D9003/9/10/12/15/18/21 had been fitted with ETH and D9001/2/5/6/13/17/19/20 were in Doncaster works for fitting, the outstanding seven locomotives being due to enter works by 28 June 1971.

Concurrent with fitting of ETH, work relating to flashover problems was being undertaken:

1. Repair of main generators and traction motors.
2. Refurbishing of control gear and renewal of associated wiring where necessary.
3. Fitting of an entirely new traction motor field divert system. Unfortunately, flashovers on the newly-fitted ETH locomotives were already arising by this time, as will be seen later. The final locomotive for fitting was the original ETH locomotive, D9007, which entered works on 7 May and left on 19 November 1971.

Overload protection was modified so that the relay would trip at a steady load of 520A with MkIId coaching stock, because the starting of the MkIId stock motor-alternator set superimposed a starting peak of 375A.

There were few troubles with the ETH in service but voltage levels down the train were low in certain operating conditions. There were no problems with voltage levels at 80mph – 90mph south of Darlington, but with speed restrictions north of that point temperatures could not be maintained due to the operational need constantly to ease-off power, it being impossible to maintain ETH voltage sufficiently to heat the train adequately. A modification was made on D9002 to enable 65mph–80mph running to heat the train adequately, using ETH voltage of 800-850V instead of 700V then in use.

In January 1971 some trains of MkIId stock had caused earth fault difficulties and, although the basic problem lay in the magnitude of the earth faults in the coaching stock, a significant feature was that the earth fault-detection equipment on Class 55 was much more sensitive than on Class 47 or on the static testing equipment, being able to sense both positive and negative earth faults.

BR Derby authorised the earth fault relay of Class 55 to be reset to trip at 500mA instead of 360mA – all locomotives to be done immediately – from February 1972. Meanwhile, it was reported that 31 main generator flashovers had occurred on ETH-fitted Class 55 locomotives between 10 October 1971 and 17 December 1971, these continuing in 1972, oil contamination being one suspected cause. By mid-1972 the position had improved somewhat, due it was thought to the modified control gear and improved generator maintenance.

During September 1973 a proposal was made to modify Class 55, so that in the event of failure of one engine ETH could still be supplied by the remaining engine; hitherto the failure of one engine resulted in no ETH provision. The modification was initiated and the final locomotive, 55017, was being done at Doncaster in January 1975.

During the summer of 1975, a number of Class 55 'lost an engine', that is an engine shut-down due to excessively high coolant temperature and therefore switched-off the ETH supply, necessary not for heating but for air-conditioning, making the coaches extremely uncomfortable for the passengers. A modification was done so that if an engine shut-down, the remaining engine would supply full ETH power equivalent to both engines, but not at idling speed.

Design work for the fitting of air braking (AB) equipment to Class 55 began in October 1967 since tests had revealed that the stopping distances required with vacuum brake for 90mph and 100mph trains was one mile and one and three-quarter miles respectively, leaving little latitude for safety on two-mile block sections of the East Coast Main Line. It was also expected that deliveries of MkII coaching stock with air braking would be

The shape of things to come as 55010 *The King's Own Scottish Borderer* heading a down express passes an up High-Speed train set near Scremeston on 10 June 1978. (*Dr L. A. Nixon*)

sufficient to form trains by October 1967. Plans to fit D9021 for test running during midsummer lapsed, and it was not until 10 October that D9016 was fitted, being closely followed by D9007. New Davies & Metcalfe compressors were fitted and initially it was feared that the extra loading on the engines would strain the phasing gears; tests, however, disproved this.

The equipment gave much initial trouble, notably with dirt in the air system, caused by corrosion (which could not be removed) in the steel pipework, blocking valves in the system; fracturing of pipework due to insufficient bracketing, and the equipment support frame in the locomotive nose being insufficiently rigid. The valves and pipework were replaced.

D9016 was virtually on air braking test runs permanently from October 1967 until early 1968, mainly on Heaton–York–Edinburgh–Heaton trips, and D9004, when fitted, on the Edinburgh–Dundee route in early 1968. The conversion programme resulted in the transfer of Class 55 locomotives to Finsbury Park as they were fitted, a short-term move but nevertheless the only official exchange involving inter-regional reallocations until 1979. D9011 was the final locomotive to receive the equipment, on 8 July 1968.

Air-braked stock was introduced from February 1968, and the need to have more than one locomotive at Doncaster works at a time resulted in the reduction of Deltic diagrams from 18 to 16 until June.

Various other problems occurred to the equipment, such as fitting new breather filters and the fitting of a modified driver's brake valve.

A persistent problem with Class 55 was slipping when starting trains in adverse rail conditions and on gradients, this condition being particularly troublesome at King's Cross, Leeds Central, and Bradford Exchange stations. Wheelslip with the Deltics convinced the regional authorities that there was something radically wrong with the locomotive control system which was too abrupt in action to enable drivers to regulate power when starting trains from rest, and when accelerating from slow speeds, EE being asked to investigate the problem. For BR J. F. Harrison suggested the fitting of an anti-slip brake working on the principle of applying the locomotive brakes when wheelslip occurred and releasing against the developed torque. At the end of 1961 EE suggested the fitting of automatic sanding gear, but pointed out that sanding should not be used when the locomotive wheels were slipping as this could give rise to axle fractures, especially if only one wheel on an axle was being sanded, a common occurrence due to blocked sanders.

A more reliable solution was applied to D9012 when EE re-profiled the air pressure control cam in the locomotive's pneumatic control system. The modification gave a steeper rise increase on the torque regulators, and the governor was adjusted so that a higher speed was attained before automatic load control commenced. This was considered successful and D9001/3/4/7/9 were similarly modified by early 1962. This was subsequently extended so that all locomotives were done by July 1962. The problem, although obviously lessened, still occurred and the same month the question of fitting an automatic wheelslip device to the Deltics was discussed. EE had such equipment in successful operation in the prototype locomotive DP2, so experience and the costing of fitting this to the Deltics was readily to hand.

BR ran dynamometer car trials with D9003 on 1 June 1962 and, following studies of the record of the run, EE said it would appear that no wheelslip had occurred. If it had, the modified system fitted to the locomotives would have quickly controlled it, and all Deltics now had the modified control cam fitted. In July 1962 it was decided to fit a wheelslip device to a Deltic locomotive.

On 30 August EE representatives travelled from Leeds to King's Cross in poor rail conditions. Persistent wheelslip occurred and 15 minutes were lost by the train between Leeds and Wakefield. The steep climb from Leeds Central to Holbeck High Level and Copley Hill caused almost continuous slipping, and passing Copley Hill Shed, the shed labourers poured a ribbon of sand on top of the rail in front of the locomotive and platelayers shovelled cinders under the wheel treads. These practices raised several issues:

1. Sand and cinders laid on one rail only.
2. Locomotive sanding important and better than the bad practice above.

An examination of Class 55 weight distribution revealed inequalities which under certain circumstances were thought likely to promote wheelslip, and $\frac{1}{4}$in shims were fitted in the bogie side bearers to remedy this.

During December 1962 D9020, fitted with an EE current-limiting device in the form of a field divert relay to limit current at low speeds, worked a 685-ton test train from King's Cross, proving successful in the 15mph to 20mph range, but not conclusive. The next step involved D9007 which was fitted with an EE anti-slip brake system in February 1963.

Control system modifications were again initiated on D9012 in October 1964 when having its annual repair, EE wishing to 'tie the ammeter to the locomotive control' and then fit test equipment and involve EE staff riding on the locomotive to observe what happened. D9012 was tried on 26 October 1964 between Leeds and King's Cross with satisfactory results. The modified controller was designed to overcome the complaints of drivers that the locomotives had difficulty in pulling away because too rapid current build-up

resulted in the overloads tripping. As modified, the controller provided a steady build-up through more increments of resistance, these being manually controlled. Automatic torque regulation did not come into effect until the locomotive reached 4mph and above, depending on train weight. Further modification was subsequently done to avoid the increased risk of flashover, which was possible on modified D9012 under certain circumstances at high speeds, but BR considered the experimental modification a success.

In May 1965 EE was asked to quote for conversion of all the locomotives, the work involving a modification of generators, governors, and controller. Subsequently, due to financial stringency, BR could not justify the conversion of the remainder of the fleet like D9012 and EE was requested to revert the locomotive back to standard at its annual examination in February 1966. EE tried in vain to get BR to modify the fleet, even by reducing their cost estimates!

Further control modifications were considered in mid 1967 as part of a general improvement scheme, and by the end of October EE was again asked to present proposals to enable the whole fleet to be done during 1968, one locomotive being done in advance for testing. The proposal included fitting a static load-regulator and by mid 1969 both EE and Brush were quoting for the equipment.

The equipment from Brush-Hawker Siddeley Dynamics Ltd was promised for delivery in January 1970, being fitted to whichever locomotive was undergoing classified repair at the time; delayed delivery resulted in one of the locomotives to be fitted for ETH being chosen. The equipment was fitted outside the locomotive control cubicle. After testing of the static load-regulator on one locomotive, with not entirely satisfactory results, further design work was put in hand. However, nothing came of this and Class 55 still retains its original EE system using an oil-driven vane motor.

In 1962 the traction motor suspension tubes were found to have flaws and modifications were put in hand by their makers. New roller bearings were fitted and no further troubles of great consequence occurred until 1977–8 when, due to the high mileages, it was decided to exchange the tubes for newer ones from Class 37, but a campaign change was not done, rather replacement as necessary. A similar scheme to

HSTs did not have it all their own way. Here in a return to former glory 55019 *Royal Highland Fusilier* with 12 MkI coaches, substitutes for the up Flying Scotsman HST, and manages to pass Finsbury Park only 31 minutes late on 12 September 1979. (*Allan C. Baker*)

exchange Class 55 traction motors for those of Class 37 followed at trial installation in 1968, at the same time as axles and wheelsets were changed.

The speeding-up of East Coast Main Line schedules during 1966 resulted in cases of damage to Class 55 water scoops when picking-up water at high speeds from water troughs. A series of modifications to strengthen the scoop mouthpieces and water deflectors and increase the speed of lowering and raising the scoop, was put in hand, involving D9003 and D9014 and test runs carried out on Wiske Moor troughs in September 1967. D9003 had a simpler modification than D9014. On the former, quick-release valves were added to the scoop's existing pneumatic system, but D9014 was provided with electrically-operated air valves for the scoop, plus an additional air reservoir. In both cases the scoop and deflector plate were similarly improved.

D9014 was tested on 13 September on the up run, taking on 290 gallons of water at 100mph, and 310 gallons at 90mph, sustaining severe scoop damage. The following day D9003 took on 300 and 190 gallons on up runs at 100mph and 250 and 190 gallons at 90mph on the down runs. On the second up and down runs the scoop was used in a slightly higher position so damage was only slight. Pending further strengthening, it was decided to fit all the class like D9003. The decision to abandon water troughs on the East Coast Main Line in January 1968 resulted in the scheme being shelved; instead, the locomotive's water capacity

was increased. To do this the engine and train-heating steam generator fuel tank was reduced from 940 to 826 gallons capacity, and the space saved together with that left by removal of the water scoop was used to increase water capacity from 640 to 830 gallons.

Diesel-electric and straight electric locomotives are always liable to experience flashovers of electrical machines and Class 55 has not proved an exception. From 1962, following freedom from flashovers apart from isolated cases, Class 55 locomotives began to experience flashovers in their traction motors as they began to exceed 90–120,000 miles service. The problem occurred mainly in the 80–85mph speed range, but the same traction motor was giving no trouble in Class 37. The motors on Class 55 had a maximum voltage of 900V but Class 37 only 450V, and of course Class 37 locomotives operated at much slower speeds and did considerably less mileage than the Class 55.

Main generator flashovers often occurred simultaneously with traction motor flashovers and Class 55 generators in series had a maximum voltage of 1800V, opposed to 900V on the Class 37. Flashovers are often difficult to resolve and traction motors and generators are prone to dirt, worn brushes, vibration, oil contamination etc, but commutator 'copper drag' was found to be the cause with Class 55. Some conflict of opinions as to what constituted 'copper drag' resulted in the problem also being described as 'stalagmites'. Regardless of terminology, the problem consisted of minute hairs or slivers of copper breaking away from, but remaining hinged at one end to, the top edge of the commutator bars and bridging the spaces between the bars, causing bar-to-bar shorting.

A thorough cleaning at depots, followed by a programme of commutator refurbishing and motor modification, plus trials with different types/grades of brushes, was put in hand during late 1962 and early 1963. The rapid mileage build up of Class 55 resulted in mileages of 200–300,000 miles by 1964, making flashovers more likely and a continuing problem. As a consequence the winter of 1964–5 saw the process of re-skimming of traction motors and generators extended, some machines having been done two and three times by the end of 1965, and by the end of 1966 the overhaul of Class 55 generators successfully eliminated flashovers on those locomotives fitted with them.

The take-over by BR of the overhaul of the motors and generators during 1968 resulted in further problems, but revision of procedures and working to more rigid standards eventually overcame these.

Oil contamination of the generators was the next problem. Following a decision in 1971 to fasten the Class 55 engine-room bodyside windows in the closed position to solve the problem of brake block dust on locomotive control gear and machines, the air flow in the engine room was completely altered. The result was a large increase in oil contamination from small oil leaks from the air manifold drains, loose pipe fittings and so on, which gave rise to an airborne mist of oil depositing a film inside the main generator. A small oil separation tank was fitted experimentally on D9018 in early 1973 which proved satisfactory so far as the air manifold was concerned, but did not take care of leaking pipework, nor oil spillage, which also contributed to contamination.

In 1972 it became clear that the Class 55 main generators being repaired at Doncaster would soon require rather heavier repairs, a deterioration in consequence of their service life, and the acceleration in deterioration caused by oil contamination. A further factor to be considered was the problem of the re-calibration of the earth fault relay (EFR). The generators were discussed at a BR meeting at Doncaster in February 1973, when it was pointed out that although the flashover problems of some 18 months previously had by now been virtually eliminated, there had been cases of flashover during ex-works trial runs, suggesting that rather more attention was now required.

The aim was to improve the condition of the generators so that they would run for 5000 hours to an intermediate repair, and 10,000 hours to a general repair. Examination of two generators stripped down at the Preston works of GEC Traction revealed that the armatures were coated with oil but were not saturated, and it was assumed that the commutators were free from oil contamination. The slot wedges were still good, but there was some fretting of end windings. It was decided that one armature taken straight from a locomotive would be sent to Derby works for detailed examination to assess the rectification work required. The work was expected to include detergent washing and vacuum impregnation, plus the possibility of glass-banding and re-wedging. An interpole core was inspected which exhibited the typical oil contamination being experienced, and in addition peeling insulation and a coil requiring a complete strip-down. Doncaster could do re-insulation and vacuum impregnation although, it being somewhat outdated, a more modern system and standard was suggested, but this was thought unjustifiable.

The main field coils were to be retaped *in situ*, but the compensating coils removed and rebuilt with some improvements, including detergent washing and vacuum impregnation. The brush-gear was found in good condition, requiring no attention.

So far as the EFR was concerned, the operational voltage of the locomotive earth fault protection system had been raised to 750V to suit the requirements of the electrically heated coaching stock. A direct consequence of this was that in the event of an earth fault developing, the generator sustained much greater damage due to the reduced level of protection. It was not the intention to alter the setting of the EFR, but rather to ensure that the generators were maintained to a more reliable standard.

By March 1973 Derby works had successfully refurbished the first armature and a specification of the work done was being prepared. In April 1973 ER stated that in spite of the introduction of the HST units, the Class 55 locomotives would remain an important part of its locomotive fleet, pointing out that unless main generator rehabilitation work was put in hand soon the future of the fleet was likely to be in jeopardy. By August 1973 ER was becoming concerned at the delay in reaching the stage when major generator work could be carried out, and the delay in producing the specification for re-insulation of the interpoles.

In November 1973 Derby Works was examining a Class 55 main generator armature which was very severely damaged. On this machine the commutator-end banding was not in evidence and the tail ends of about half of the coils had lifted and appeared to have been torn off by the rotation of the machine. Two large craters had been burnt in the laminated core beneath the missing coils and a number of commutator segments had been badly burnt. There were also holes burnt in the core and coils. The damage was such that only the hollow shaft casting of the armature was re-usable.

Maintenance procedures were questioned, but it was pointed out that the machines were examined monthly due to their intensive usage, and that it was only since the conversion of Class 55 to supply ETH that severe generator troubles had arisen.

The environment in which the generators worked was unusual compared to those of other BR locomotive types, the Class 55 being unique in that ETH for the trains was supplied by the main generator, the EFR being tripped by both faults in the locomotive and earth faults in any coach of the train it was hauling.

One consequence of this was that the designed traction EFR settings on Class 55 had been altered to approximate to train heat fault relays on other types of locomotives. If this was not done, trains hauled by other than Class 55 locomotives could not continue their journey when the locomotive was replaced by a Class 55, should there be an earth leakage on the train which was too small to be detected by the ETH earth fault relay of the previous locomotive, but large enough to be detected by the traction EFR as originally set. In such a situation the Class 55 traction EFR would continually trip and no traction power be possible. The result was that with small earth faults on the train the Class 55 locomotives' generators were subjected to a strain of far greater magnitude than normal on traction machines, and that in the event of an earth fault on the generator developing, it increased more rapidly than normal.

Although this problem had been appreciated as a likely consequence of altering the EFR setting, making it less sensitive, no other solution in the time available was feasible. The alteration in effect sacrificed the power earth fault protection on the locomotive in order to permit them to haul ETH-fitted trains, but the frequency of main generator damage had not been realised. In December 1973 it was stated that at least twelve cases of main generator damage had taken place since September 1972, at a repair cost of approximately £20,000. The fact that the Class 55 generators were suffering such severe damage was in part due to their age and condition resulting from intensive service, and it was considered that the major overhaul of the machines would decrease the severity of the damage, although not the incidence. The supply of armatures was by mid-December 1973 becoming very tight indeed with seven under repair/rewind, and only two available for fitting to spare power units, and to implement glass-banding and vacuum impregnation processes. One of the latest failures involved an armature which had been glass-banded, TIG-welded and vacuum-impregnated at Derby, and had only been in service for 40 hours, posing doubts about the efficacy of the major overhaul to reduce damage – especially since the machine concerned had badly burnt windings and armature laminations, together with commutator damage.

On 28 December 1973 the BRB CME stated that a modification to Class 55 ETH system was possible, involving automatic conversion of the EFR system to its original sensitivity during those periods when the locomotive was not hauling ETH stock, and D9021 was modified and tested at Doncaster works by 8 January 1974, proving successful. Following the fitting of four further locomotives, a programme was initiated so that one locomotive per day would visit Doncaster works for the modification, the work being completed on 29 January 1974.

The comparatively simple modification lessened the toll on the generators and allowed the generator rehabilitation programme to continue at both Derby works and the Preston works of GEC Traction.

CLASS 55
AVERAGE MILES PER CASUALTY AND TARGET MILEAGE 1971–80
Four-week periods (some periods missing)

Period	Mileage	Target
30.1.71	9323	14000
27.2.71	8736	14000
27.3.71	8622	14000
24.4.71	8436	14000
27.5.71	11642	14000
19.6.71	19671	14000
17.7.71	14058	14000
14.8.71	11149	14000
11.9.71	10999	13000
9.10.71	14728	13000
6.11.71	19711	13000
4.12.71	10488	13000
1.1.72	38900	15000
29.1.72	8705	15000
26.2.72	13034	15000
25.3.72	13011	15000
22.4.72	22813	15000
20.5.72	13825	15000
15.7.72	11866	15000
12.8.72	11325	15000
9.9.72	13345	15000
7.10.72	19600	15000
2.12.72	10745	15000
30.12.72	31423	15000
27.1.73	16348	15000
24.2.73	13350	15000
21.4.73	28778	15000
19.5.73	15620	15000
16.6.73	13676	15000
14.7.73	21649	15000
11.8.73	12577	14000–16000
8.9.73	10960	14000–16000
6.10.73	15963	14000–16000
3.11.73	16339	14000–16000
1.12.73	13252	14000–16000
29.12.73	17711	14000–16000
26.1.74	19463	15000
23.2.74	23818	15000
20.4.74	24747	15000
18.5.74	24415	15000
15.6.74	17501	15000
13.7.74	20950	15000
10.8.74	17880	15000
7.9.74	11415	15000
5.10.74	13381	15000
2.11.74	17173	15000
30.11.74	16597	15000
28.12.74	14247	15000
25.1.75	12034	15000
22.2.75	10896	15000
19.4.75	14370	15000
17.5.75	10261	15000
14.6.75	17937	15000
12.7.75	13311	15000
9.8.75	8811	15000
6.9.75	11046	15000
4.10.75	15467	15000
1.11.75	13218	15000
29.11.75	11128	15000
3.1.76	13555	15000
31.1.76	11801	15000
28.2.76	23590	15000
27.3.76	16074	15000
24.4.76	8520	15000
25.5.76	14769	15000
19.6.76	17204	15000
14.8.76	13965	15000
11.9.76	15578	15000
9.10.76	14880	15000
6.11.76	15651	15000
4.12.76	13563	15000
1.1.77	12329	15000
29.1.77	9114	15000
26.2.77	13472	15000
24.3.77	15028	15000
23.4.77	18229	15000
21.5.77	12850	15000
18.6.77	11832	15000
13.8.77	25078	15000
10.9.77	18550	15000
8.10.77	14955	15000
5.11.77	12979	15000
3.12.77	14602	15000
31.12.77	17174	15000
28.1.78	10241	15000
25.2.78	11242	15000
25.3.78	12736	15000
22.4.78	14407	15000
20.6.78	8751	15000
17.7.78	14153	15000
12.8.78	11271	15000
9.9.78	11214	15000
7.10.78	12190	15000
4.11.78	15633	15000
2.12.78	9818	15000
30.12.78	9076	15000
21.1.79	7076	15000
24.2.79	6519	15000
24.3.79	7215	15000
21.4.79	7785	15000
19.5.79	11594	15000
16.6.79	8032	15000
8.79	11291	15000
9.79	10993	15000
10.79	8640	15000
11.79	8695	15000
12.79	6641	15000
13.79	6510	15000
1.80	6130	15000
2.80	4964	15000

CHAPTER 9

DELTIC REFURBISHING, WORKINGS, AND DECLINE

During 1967 consideration was given to rehabilitating Class 55 and accordingly EE was asked to submit its proposals and cost estimates to BR. Naturally EE envisaged doing the work at VF, commencing in August 1968, the main proposals being as follows.

The complete locomotive superstructures were to be sent carriage paid by BR to VF on accommodation bogies, BR retaining the bogies for rehabilitation at Doncaster. BR was to supply EE with drawings of the dual brake equipment fitted by BR, plus pipe runs etc, for reference.

EE was to work on one locomotive at a time, EE estimates covering removal and re-installation of equipment, rewiring, cleaning, painting and testing. The estimates did not include reconditioning of various machines which could only be costed after stripping and examination.

The detailed proposal covered all items of equipment and fittings which were to be removed entirely for rehabilitation and permit inspection and cleaning of the whole superstructure inside and out.

The power units were to go complete to Napier's works, which would remove and send the main

generator/auxiliary generator to EE at Preston; EE would also undertake work on the control cubicles, fuel pumps and motors, driving control gear. VF was to carry out the work on the superstructures, water, fuel and header tanks, check all gauges and return faulty ones to BR, test and clean all pipework, rehabilitate engine silencers, roof sections, check all power cables, replacing faulty ones. BR was to do the radiators, radiator fan drives, and gearboxes, batteries, cab seats, windscreen wipers, fire extinguishers, CO_2 bottles, and air filters. Equipment such as steam generators, compressors and exhausters were to be dealt with by their respective manufacturers.

It was proposed that EE would install electric train heating, driven from the main generators and associated equipment/control gear, modify the locomotive control gear so that it was similar to that to be used in the proposed Class 50, ie static load regulator, static voltage regulator and wheelslip control.

Complete repainting was to follow removal of the existing paint system and then wheeling and connection to the rehabilitated bogies supplied by BR to VF, and finally to test the locomotives at VF. The proposal was dated 8 December 1967.

The suggestion that EE should carry out this did not meet with BR approval as it wished to do all the work at Doncaster. The question of refurbishing was based on the need for Class 55 to operate satisfactorily for another five to seven years; there was, however, no suggestion in the

Deltic triumphant, but business as usual as 55003 *Meld* smokes-out King's Cross station when departing on the down Hull Executive on 14 May 1979. The Finsbury Park 'racehorses' were adorned with white cab roofs and window surrounds during 1979, and in this instance a specially-made train headboard was provided. The Hull Executive was claimed as the fastest British locomotive-hauled train ever. (*Roger Newling-Goode*)

After 55016, 55019 *Royal Highland Fusilier* was the second Class 55 to receive refurbishing at Doncaster works during 1976. Here it heads a running-in turn from York to Darlington near Hutton Bonville on a misty 27 May 1980. (*Brian Webb*)

then 'National Traction Plan' to withdraw the locomotives, although at the time their reliability was deteriorating. The cost of rehabilitation, said to be over £25,000 per locomotive, aroused doubts within the ER, which thought that a more substantial justification for the cost must be made.

On 23 February 1968 the Eastern Region CM&EE set out some reasons for rehabilitation. It was felt that Class 55 was now approaching the stage when a more thorough overhaul than normal was necessary, but that any major expenditure must not only produce a more advanced locomotive but also lead to considerable reduction in casualties by eliminating those present features giving most trouble. In support of this a summary of the main problems causing casualties over a recent 24-week period were listed:

Casualties	Number of cases
Control equipment	38
Spanner steam generator	23
Main generators	9
Cables	8
Engines	6
Traction motors	5
Fuel system	4
Other electrical equipment	4
Air compressor	4
Brake system	4
Other carriage warming equipment	4
Miscellaneous	11
	120

The nature of the cause of Class 55 casualties had changed over the years. During the early life of the locomotives many were due to design defects which had been slowly overcome. The fitting of air brakes, which started on 7 October 1967, brought new problems, and ageing of components was

Defects	Number of cases
Control equipment	15
Main generators	8
Cooling system	6
Instruments	5
Miscellaneous	26
	60

likely to become more prominent in the analysis of casualties. The class had only been in service for six years, but it had achieved a very high mileage at a rate about twice that of any other locomotive class. Consequently, the cumulative effect of vibration was starting to show. Class 55 had suffered twice the number of stress reversals of any other class. In addition to casualties, ingress of dirt into control cubicles, cracking and distortion of body panels, chafing of cables and deterioration of cable insulation, work-hardening of copper wire in coils, wear in contactors and relays, and draughts from sliding windows, required attention.

To allow for a decision upon the work required – design work, ordering of material and its delivery – the following time scale was suggested: decide and complete design tasks, June–December 1968, and begin modification of first locomotive in October 1969, which would then be run in traffic before any more were rehabilitated, to identify teething troubles. In order to progress the design tasks some questions required an answer:

1. Was water pick-up equipment still required? If removed, what additional water capacity would be required if water were to be taken from water cranes only? Could water treatment be controlled to avoid the need to provide chemical dosage equipment which had been the cause of casualties?
2. Was ETH required?
3. Would the steam generator be required by 1970?

4. Would vacuum brake be necessary in 1970?
5. Was a higher maximum speed required in 1970?

In order to obtain information on the condition of Class 55 and enable costings to be obtained, it was decided to take one locomotive into Doncaster works as an exercise to determine future overhaul requirements, and D9016 was selected.

At a meeting held on 18 September 1968 the proposal for a general repair was discussed and it was decided that D9016 would receive a thorough inspection and repair, including the fitting of new traction motors from stock, a policy recommended for the rest of Class 55, the displaced motors being overhauled for use on Class 37. D9016 entered works on 26 September 1968 and was ex-works on 8 November 1968 after the following work:

1. Dual brake reservoirs beneath driver's seats removed.
2. Header tank for urinal heavily corroded internally. Tank removed, repaired, repainted.
3. Six new traction motors fitted. Motors taken from stores and dried-out in conveyor oven prior to fitting.
4. Field divert resistances. One end set removed, cleaned and refitted. Due to inaccessibility other end set not removed.
5. Checking of field divert resistances.
6. Load regulator resistance values checked at one end.
7. Control cubicle equipment removed, stripped and cleaned, then refitted. The following points were raised:
   a. Necessity to remove only auxiliary contact assemblies for cleaning.
   b. Adjustable relays (eg wheelslip satisfactory, others requiring removal for cleaning and overhaul due to poor accessibility in situ.
   c. Air-operated contactors for traction motors, field diversion main generator cut-out switches and reversers, required complete overhaul. Links worn, cylinders dry and corroded.
   d. Circuit breakers required replacement. Only two out of eight renewed on D9016 due to stock position. Displaced ones showed wear when examined.
   e. Plugs and sockets examined in situ and found satisfactory. Works was reluctant to disconnect plugs for examination and suggest a new type.
8. Cables satisfactory — no renewals necessary.
9. Cab heater and cabling all right.
10. Crimps — terminals renewed in one cubicle by cutting back the cable. Shortage of time to do other cubicle.
11. Load regulator oil pipes renewed.
12. Painting of cubicle not done as cleaning found adequate.
13. Frame examination — visible examination only. Strain gauging necessary to be sure.
14. Air brake equipment removed and overhauled.

From this a recommended procedure was drawn up, based on the following:

1. No comment.
2. All tanks to be removed and treated.
3. All new traction motors ex-stores to be dried out by one pass through stoving oven, having first been stripped of armature and carcase, which should pass through separately. Commutator to be modified, ie vee cuttered along the slots.
4. Field divert resistances to be visually checked as far as visibility permits and only removed if defective.
5. Doncaster works claimed no adjustment necessary to field divert resistances. Probably not necessary to check all locomotives.
6. All load regulator resistances to be checked.
7. Control cubicle:
   a. Remove all auxiliary contact assemblies for cleaning and overhaul.
   b. No work necessary, but remove all inaccessible relays for complete overhaul and cleaning.
   c. Remove all air-operated contactors for stripping and overhaul.
   d. Replace all circuit breakers with improved pattern.
   e. Fit new pattern plugs and sockets.
8. All cabling to be examined and renewed where necessary.
9. Examine cab heater and cables visually, renew where required.
10. Where equipment is taken out of control cubicle, all cable connections should be re-crimped. Repair where necessary.
11. Renewal of pipework being done at

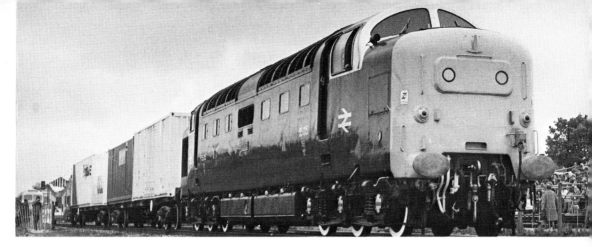

A thoroughbred on parade. 55015 *Tulyar* specially turned-out by Finsbury Park depot, with an unusual train at the Rocket 150 celebrations at Rainhill on 25 May 1980. Note plated-over leading cabside window. (*Roger Newling-Goode*)

intermediate repairs. To remove pipes and test was only a requirement for the next three years.
12. Cleanliness of cubicle is the only important feature.
13. Strain gauge testing of frame would give a more reliable appraisal of the situation.
14. All brake valves to be removed and fully overhauled.

On 10 February 1969 D9010 was taken out of service with severe bodyside fractures on the assistant's side of No 2 end cab. Fractures were not uncommon and repair by welding in new support angles or new body skin sections was adopted. This problem has continued to be dealt with in this way as it arose.

Nothing else was done regarding Class 55 rehabilitation until March 1971 when a meeting discussed the question of the life span of the class, especially in connection with spares. The meeting held at Doncaster stated that the booked life for Class 55 was until 1986, and that the only components thought likely to require repairs in excess of the normal level of classified repairs were the locomotive superstructures and electrical machines; the latter would require above average attention during 1975–8, together with the Spanner steam generator.

The extent of superstructure corrosion inside the bodysides had been more clearly defined as a result of an exercise done by removal of the inner skin of 55008. The corrosion was not as bad as feared, so could be dealt with when the locomotives were modified for ETH. Corroded platework around the bodyside windows was to be renewed as necessary and new window seals fitted

to stop further ingress of moisture. D9008 was in works for fitting of ETH during the late summer of 1971, but in spite of the investigation it was not refurbished.

In spite of repeated requests, the proposals languished until 1973–4 when BRB CM&EE was investigating an outline procedure for a campaign overhaul of Class 55. However, it was not until the autumn of 1975 that once again detailed investigation by BR and GEC Traction at Doncaster into the general repair proposal was undertaken. Co-incidentally, 55016 was again chosen as the subject under investigation. Since this locomotive had been in works since 5 July 1975 awaiting engines during a severe engine shortage, it was decided that it would receive the first general repair.

Bearing in mind the inspection of 55008 body panelling and the fact that no more Class 55 had been similarly inspected, it was decided that 55016 would be similarly inspected. On this locomotive it was again discovered that in general the condition of most of the inner face of the bodyside panelling was quite good, not requiring replacement. A new painting specification was used on this and the protective lining and inner skin replaced. In addition, the floor beneath the steam generator was cut out and renewed, and the redundant sand filler gear in the floor and bodysides was plated-over. The cabside windows were dealt with to avoid draughts, water entry, and loose window frames, by vertical stiffening, involving blanking-out by steel sheet of the triangular-shape first cabside window, a modification subsequently extended. Complaints about draughty cab doors were found to be due largely to the fact that the sliding door tracks and seals had not received adequate maintenance since the locomotives were new, but the doors themselves were in good condition, making renewal unjustified. More attention was to be given to door surrounds at

The York–King's Cross 'slows' or stopping trains became Deltic territory from 1979, 55004 *Queen's Own Highlander* leans to the curve at Riccall with the 15.50 from York on 24 July 1980. (*Brian Webb*)

general and classified repairs. It was thought that when the modification to cab airflow, as tried on 55005 in 1975, was applied to all locomotives, the problem of draughty doors would be overcome. Plans to fit headlights were not pursued but removal of the 4-digit route indicators was approved.

Although a number of other matters were included in the general repair proposal, following experience with 55016 (which had left Doncaster works on 27 April 1976) it was decided that it was not necessary to undertake work of this magnitude on other locomotives of the class, but rather to do those necessary to keep the fleet in action to comply with the booked life. Attention was therefore to be concentrated on cab windows, cab doors, cab airflow, illumination of cab instruments, improvements in pipework, brake switches, route indicator removal, control gear, coolant header tanks, and windscreen wipers.

During the autumn of 1972 the conversion of Class 55 route indicator boxes to show two circular discs started with D9009 being fitted at

From May 1980 there were two daily Deltic diagrams on the Anglo-Scottish services between King's Cross and Edinburgh. The 10.52 from Edinburgh is seen thundering across Plawsworth viaduct with 55017 *The Durham Light Infantry* on 16 May 1980. (*Brian Webb*)

Finsbury Park depot on 28 September. Various combinations were tried until in July 1974 the elimination of the 4-digit route indicator, and fitting of black-and-white printed screens on the inside of the box glass, with two 7in diameter white discs at 2ft $9\frac{3}{4}$in centres, was approved for the whole class. Further variations on this theme have subsequently appeared on Class 55 as well as other BR locomotive classes. Only five locomotives did in fact receive general repairs. 55019 was given a part body check on its interior, but received a full general repair, arriving in works on 27 January 1976. The remaining three 55002/13/21 arrived in Doncaster works on 16 March, 25 May, and 22 April 1976 respectively, all receiving a full 'general' without body interior attention. Since that time Class 55 has only had intermediate repairs.

The decision to cease the official recording of Class 55 locomotive mileages on 27 March 1976, when the fleet total stood at a staggering 54,700,000 miles, was unfortunate. However, it has been possible to arrive at a reliable figure calculated by the ER CM&EE, so that at the end of 1980 the fleet mileage was approximately 63,800,000.

The intention to put 42 High-Speed Trains (HST) into service on the East Coast Main Line was announced in 1975 and this obviously influenced the above decision on Class 55. The HSTs to many heralded the demise of the Class 55 locomotives. However, government cutbacks in BR

investment reduced this to 32 HSTs, and in early 1976 the ER expressed concern over the necessity to continue to provide locomotive-hauled trains.

It was recognised that there would be a continuing requirement for Class 55, or at least part of the fleet, until the 1980s. In February 1976 G. S. W. Calder, then the BRB CM&EE, envisaged all the locomotives being out of service by 1982. As soon as the HST fleet became available, the Class 55 fleet would be downgraded for use on slower, overnight services at an 80mph limit, and the locomotive-hauled trains running among the HSTs would be based on Class 47 or Class 50 locomotives with loads of eight vehicles (280 tons), and nine vehicles (315 tons) respectively. These did not equate with Class 55 315-ton timings, and pathing difficulties were likely to result. ER evidence supporting the retention of Class 55 on top link work was submitted, in the form of a report on the under-powering of class 1 trains due to the provision of less suitable locomotives. A single 24-hour mid-week period was examined to ascertain the root of the problem. Of forty-one trains booked for Class 55 haulage, only twenty-five were so covered. The

sixteen trains covered by Class 47 and the resulting cascading of trouble caused eight trains booked for Class 47 to be downgraded further to Class 40 haulage, and two trains booked for Class 40 to be hauled by Class 37. Difficulties were experienced in providing sufficient ETH-equipped locomotives, and of the twenty-two Class 55 the following situation existed:

55002/13/19/21	In Doncaster works.
55004/10	Depot repairs.
55003	Repairs at Finsbury Park – out of service for more than 12 hours.
55007	'C' examination at Finsbury Park – out of service for more than 12 hours.
55015	'B' examination and steam generator repairs at Finsbury Park – out of service for more than 12 hours.

The following were out of service for between two to seven hours:

Locomotive class		55		50		47		50		47	
Load (tons)		350		315		315		280		280	
Speed (mph)		100		100		95		100		95	
		Min	Sec	Min	Sec	Min	Sec	Min	Sec	Min	Sec
King's Cross	dep	—	—	—	—	—	—	—	—	—	—
Huntingdon	stop	43	3	45	5	46	4	44	6	45	7
Peterborough	stop	14	4	15	4	15	6	14	9	15	1
Grantham	stop	21	9	23	6	23	8	22	8	23	1
Newark	stop	11	5	11	8	12	2	11	7	12	0
Retford	stop	15	3	16	3	16	5	15	8	15	9
Doncaster	stop	15	7	16	4	16	5	16	1	16	2
Selby	stop	15	4	16	4	16	7	15	9	16	0
York	arr	14	4	15	1	15	2	14	8	14	8
	TOTAL	148	39	157	35	159	39	151	56	156	28
York	dep	—	—	—	—	—	—	—	—	—	—
Selby	stop	14	0	14	7	14	8	14	4	14	4
Doncaster	stop	16	0	17	0	17	1	16	6	16	7
Retford	stop	15	8	16	5	16	6	16	2	16	2
Newark	stop	15	6	16	6	16	7	16	2	16	3
Grantham	stop	12	9	13	9	13	9	13	4	13	4
Peterborough	stop	21	5	22	5	23	1	22	1	22	6
Huntingdon	stop	14	7	15	7	15	8	15	2	15	3
King's Cross	arr	44	2	46	6	47	3	45	4	46	1
	TOTAL	151	37	159	45	161	43	157	25	158	30

55004 *Queen's Own Highlander* roars through Croft Spa with the Sunday 14.53 Newcastle–Doncaster on 16 May 1980. (*Brian Webb*)

55008	'C' examination and injector change at Gateshead
55009	In Doncaster works.
55014	Checks for loose tyres at Finsbury Park.
55016	Repairs to No. 1 engine at Haymarket.

In service: 55001/5/6/11/12/17/18/20/22.

A table comparing timings for trains stopping at all stations to York based on permanent speed limits applicable on 18 May 1975 was prepared by the ER during April 1976:

A further investment submission for ten more HSTs for the East Coast Main Line included as an investment alternative the use of locomotive-hauled trains along with the authorised 32 HSTs. At the time some confidence was expressed in getting the ten extra trains, but this quickly changed to the mixed services alluded to. The National Traction Plan was revised somewhat, and proposals assumed the use of Class 55, not Classes

During 1980 high Class 55 availability resulted in more being in traffic than diagrammed, so they were used on trains to a number of unusual places. 55011 *The Royal Northumberland Fusiliers* with one nameplate missing, approaches Cayton on the Scarborough–Hull line with empty stock to form the 08.54 (SO) Filey–Newcastle on 30 August 1980, the locomotive working the train between Filey and Scarborough prior to taking its own duty, the 09.54 Scarborough–King's Cross. (*Brian Webb*)

47 or 50, quite the reverse of the thinking over the previous twelve months or so.

In April 1976 further consideration on the possible use of Class 55 along with the HSTs was being studied. ER requirements stated that locomotive-hauled services from King's Cross to Humberside could not be operated by any other locomotive than Class 55 without impairing HST timekeeping. G. S. W. Calder had no objection to the use of Class 55 during the initial years of HST operation, '. . . on the understanding that they will be withdrawn in the early 1980s. Latest date for withdrawal of the Deltics should be planned for 1982.'

The deteriorating condition of the Class 55 mechanical parts – notably the superstructures – caused concern in 1976 when some cabside windows were blown out in traffic, due to the life expiry of the rubber strips between the body skin and the aluminium window frames. The fitting of new rubber strips overcame this. Fracturing of the body skins at the cabside windows was affecting most of the Deltics. The worst of these occurred between the top of the rear cabside windows where fractures ran diagonally to the door aperture, and from the lower corner of the window. Welding and patching was again employed to repair the locomotives. By April 1977 the traction withdrawal plan showed that 1980–2 was the period for Class 55 withdrawal. This was part of a rolling programme of locomotive replacement but depended on the introduction of 42 HSTs, and

discussions for the final ten of these were then still in progress, so Class 55 withdrawal was likely to be spread over a longer period. When Mr K. Taylor became BRB CM&EE he asked the ER to state its requirements for Class 55 so that spares could be provided correctly for the run-down period of the fleet. In May 1977 it was decided that withdrawal would be:

Year	Number of locomotives
1980	2
1981	5
1982	5
1983	5
1984	5

This it was felt would cover all or most eventualities and provide the basis for spares planning. It was thought that the pressing problem of provision of train-heating steam generators in working order on Class 55 would be overcome by the end of 1980 when all East Coast sleeping cars should be converted to electric train heating.

In July 1978 the Eastern Region approached the Scottish Region on the programme for Class 55 diagrams after May 1979. Plans were to use them on King's Cross – Hull, King's Cross – York, with very few workings north of York to Newcastle and Edinburgh, creating problems of putting Gateshead and Haymarket locomotives through their home depots for routine maintenance requirements. From an operating point of view all the locomotives would be better based at one or two ER depots – possibly Finsbury Park and York. Difficulty would arise in finding the expertise essential to maintain reliability with these locomotives. Reallocation was to be from May 1979.

The ER CM&EE decided that from January 1979 the fourteen ER locomotives would work to a target availability of 50%. This was realistic, being based on actual ER Class 55 performance in the past few months. This had little chance of immediate improvement, bearing in mind the engine problems and limited production of overhauled engines from Doncaster works. The Scottish Region agreed to the proposals.

During early 1979 the future of Finsbury Park depot was in doubt, due largely to the reduction in locomotive-hauled trains. It was intended to reduce its allocation to diesel shunters and only carry out servicing and minor repairs from May 1980; however, the time scale was extended until May 1981.

The withdrawal programme had been reassessed on a year-by-year requirement by discussion between BRB and ER:

Year ending	Number of locomotives		
	in service	available	to be withdrawn
1979	22	12	0
1980	19	11	3
1981	17	10	2
1982	12	7	5
1983	7	4	5
1984	0	0	7

In view of the lower annual mileages the 'residual Deltics' would be covering year by year, the withdrawal rate did not need to be absolutely rigid, provided that some were withdrawn each year and the final date of 1984 was not exceeded. At this time an embryo LMR proposal to use Class 55 on a high-speed service between Sheffield and St Pancras pending extension of the Midland main line electrification was being considered, and it was possible that a positive outcome could affect the scrapping rate. The long period that 55001/20 had spent at Doncaster works ultimately led to the decision to withdraw them in view of the very considerable work and components needed to return them to traffic.

During the latter part of 1980 the deteriorating financial position of BR, aggravated by the decline of UK industry, caused much re-thinking regarding motive power requirements. The outcome was selective storage and withdrawal of motive power, the Class 55 and their future being seriously affected. Their programmed withdrawal was drastically curtailed from the end of 1984 to May 1982.

At the end of 1980 55009 was to be the final Deltic locomotive to receive a classified repair, and only two further Deltic engines would be overhauled. Withdrawal of locomotives would of course depend on their condition, but the position was certainly bleak, and the fact that the class would lose its remaining diagrams in May 1981 looked very ominous.

On 31 December 1980 55003 was withdrawn – it was the third locomotive scheduled for 1980 – its bogies being required for use on Class 37, but at the same time providing further spares for its own family. During January 1981, after the introduction of additional HST services, it was becoming difficult to employ the locomotives, the future was indeed bleak, some doubts being

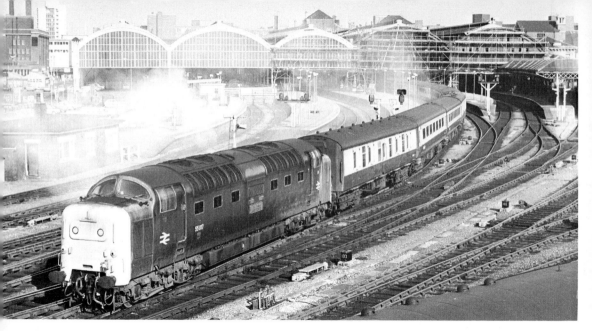

From May 1979 Class 55 began working Hull–King's Cross services. Here 55017 *The Durham Light Infantry* leaves Hull Paragon station with the 16.30 to King's Cross on 9 September 1980. (*Les Bertram*)

expressed as to whether or not they would last long enough to see the end of 1981.

The performance capability of Class 55 locomotives has received much coverage over the years, and many experts have analysed and argued about their work since introduction into traffic. Their performance is not covered at all in this study, rather their impact on the East Coast Main Line timetables. The first improvements were in June 1962 when, celebrating the centenary of The Flying Scotsman service, 6-hour schedules were introduced on Anglo-Scottish services between King's Cross and Edinburgh. Intensive diagramming, involving 20 diagrams, was introduced in the 1962–3 winter timetable, leaving only two spare locomotives for all eventualities.

It was, however, the gradual improvement of the East Coast route itself by removing curves, slewing of track etc, which had the greatest effect in extracting Class 55 potential. In 1966 with 100mph permitted on some sections of line, the fastest-ever King's Cross–Leeds run, $185\frac{3}{4}$ miles in 160 minutes at an average of almost 70mph, and King's Cross–Edinburgh, 399 miles in 350 minutes at an average of 67.3mph, were timetabled.

March 1967 saw the diagrams recast to give more concentrated running, eliminating spare locomotives at King's Cross, Newcastle, and Edinburgh, requiring only eighteen locomotives

daily – six from each depot – but with the locomotives accomplishing one more round trip each. The introduction of air-braked coaching stock, and the programme of fitting the locomotives for this, resulted in early 1968 in a reduction of their diagrams.

The completion of the 1970–1 stage of East Coast track improvements resulted in 180 miles of the $268\frac{1}{2}$ King's Cross–Newcastle mileage being available for 100mph running. Accordingly, Darlington at 232 miles was reached in 179 minutes; Newcastle $268\frac{1}{2}$ miles in 215 minutes; and Leeds $185\frac{3}{4}$ miles in 159 minutes. Trains between King's Cross and Newcastle varied between 215 and 220 minutes running time, depending on the number of stops. This timetable brought with it the first claims that Class 55 was exceeding its rated output by putting out 3125hp, much more than their 2640 rail hp rating, at 85% efficiency. In 1974 the Newcastle Executive was given 212 minutes, including a 2-minute stop at Darlington, to cover the $268\frac{1}{2}$ miles to King's Cross.

The introduction of the HST in 1979 was seen as the death knell for Class 55 as top link locomotives, their work being south of York except for some overnight trains and the 0550 King's Cross–Aberdeen. Their use on the Hull services, notably the Hull Executive, called on them to operate their best schedule ever – the fastest-ever locomotive-hauled train in the UK. This train had to average 91.4mph between King's Cross and Retford, but as the keen-eyed had noticed, the Sunday equivalent of this train was timed to cover the 77.85 miles between Stevenage and Grantham in 50 minutes, giving an average of 93.4mph! Although BR will not confirm it officially, one locomotive achieved 120mph on test in 1961 and the test was only terminated because of the whistling of the traction motors. However, service speeds of 105mph are not uncommon. Traction motors are subject to a test-bed overspeed of 30% to prove the mechanical integrity of the armature. So high speeds of 110mph to 115mph are within the traction motor capability, but at the expense of eating into the safety margin.

The HST services of 1979 were upset by the blockage of Penmanshiel tunnel and provision of a connecting bus service between Berwick and Dunbar, with a handful of services being re-routed via Carlisle and Carstairs. The 0550 to Aberdeen was one of these and thus an almost daily Deltic was to be seen on Beattock in daylight, although the locomotives are by no means strangers, especially on the Sunday morning sleepers which have come through Carlisle for some time, and were regularly booked for Class 55 haulage until 1980.

Spare Class 55s find their way on to King's Cross–Cleethorpes, King's Cross–Leeds (deputising for non-available HSTs), Newcastle–Liverpool, York–Edinburgh on the Plymouth trains, and in 1980 on the Saturdays-only Scarborough–King's Cross, while their official activities again took in King's Cross–Edinburgh workings during 1980, plus the York and Hull diagrams. For some reason Class 47 stray into the Class 55 diagrams, and if a train is late the culprit is often found to be a Class 47 looking 'hot and bothered' with the effort being made to deputise! Their use on enthusiasts' specials and other odd workings have taken them to many other places outside their normal spheres of operation.

CHAPTER 10

DELTIC POSSIBILITIES

The application of the Deltic engine to rail traction in the 1955 prototype *Deltic* locomotive could well have been its only application on rail if it had not been for Gerald F. Fiennes, the BR ER Line Traffic Manager. The 9-cylinder Deltic engine had been authorised for use in the ten Baby Deltics of 1100hp under the pilot scheme, but it was unlikely to be reordered for such low-power locomotives intended for very secondary duties when simpler competitive designs were available. It was therefore against a background of some top-level BTC reluctance that Fiennes managed to push through his requirement for twenty-two 3300hp locomotives.

In spite of the success of the 3300hp locomotives in revolutionising the East Coast Main Line services and proving fallacious once and for all the argument that 2000hp was sufficient for a BR main line diesel, the Deltic engine sadly failed as a commercial rail traction power unit, in spite of being a decade ahead of the competition. The reasons for its failure have been aired many times and are too numerous to pursue here. They included clashes of personality, and loyalties expressed in the view of some EE diesel engine division men who, rightly in their view, saw the only solution to demands for higher power outputs as the further development of the remarkably successful EE medium-speed diesel engine. D. Napier & Sons Ltd, although part of the EE group, was considered a newcomer with no rail traction experience, said to have been regarded as a 'foreigner' trying to enter rail traction at EE, hitherto the sole domain of EE Diesel Engines. Thank goodness those at the helm of EE had their say! Whether or not this was factual, I know not.

It has been said that a similar situation existed at BR, where in some quarters the Deltic engine was considered a very queer fish indeed. This, coupled with a reluctance to accept high-speed (rev/min) non-standard engines (a criticism often levelled at engineers) made the engine seem undesirable. The advantages the Deltic engine offered – high power, small size, low weight – seemed to be just what railways needed, and indeed many design proposals for a number of countries were prepared by EE for Deltic-engined locomotives and, interestingly, to a lesser degree for BR.

In the heyday of the diesel-hydraulic which offered railways a comparatively light engine and transmission system in a lightweight locomotive mechanical structure, the Deltic engine enabled EE to offer a very competitive diesel-electric locomotive to weights hitherto only attainable with diesel-hydraulics.

Of the design proposals prepared for BR, only one has been made public, namely the 4400–4600hp Super Deltic of the 1960s, but there were others, some of which are illustrated here.

During 1957 EE prepared three alternatives for the BR Type 3 range using the Deltic 18-cylinder rated at 1700hp and of Bo-Bo design. All weighed 72 tons, two were of twin cab/nose layout, but the third was the BR hood-type Bo-Bo of EE design, now known as Class 20. The following year when the WR was still in the midst of its diesel-hydraulic honeymoon, EE took the unusual step of preparing a design of 1700hp with two conventional 6-cylinder or 8-cylinder EE engines, or one 12-cylinder or 16-cylinder EE engine and allied these to the Mekhydro transmission within a

C-C bogie design. BR was interested, needing some 300 Type 3 diesels. It was then that the obvious advantage of the Deltic engine was again realised, and by November a 74-ton B-B with two Deltic 9-cylinder engines, each rated at 850hp to give 1700hp via the Mekhydro transmission, was ready for consideration.

Another 1958 project for BR originated from queries made by BR as to whether EE could produce designs for a 2500hp diesel electric locomotive to meet the need for a more powerful locomotive than current 2000/2300hp 1Co-Co1 designs. EE considered a number of proposals of 125–135 tons weight and with standard EE Vee-type conventional engines in what was virtually the EE BR Type 4 or Class 40 mechanical design. An alternative range of Bo-Bo or Co-Co type with two Deltic 9-cylinder or one Deltic 18-cylinder engine, weighing in the 72-ton to 99-ton band was also designed. The Bo-Bo was of four variants, three with the 18-cylinder engine, weighing 72, 76, and 78 tons, the weight variation being due to the type of train-heating fitted. The fourth had two 9-cylinder engines and weighed 79 tons. The Co-Co with two 9-cylinder engines was virtually a shortened prototype Deltic, two variants with different train-heating being proposed, weighing 96 and 99 tons. BR was interested in quotations

Fig A. A 1957 Deltic 18-cylinder engine alternative to the English Electric Type 3 (Class 37) in the form of a 1700hp 72-ton Bo-Bo. (*GEC Traction Ltd*)

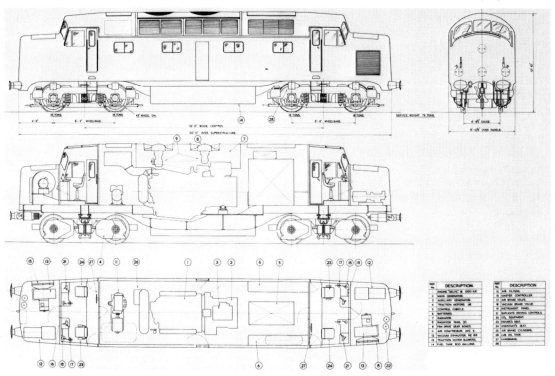

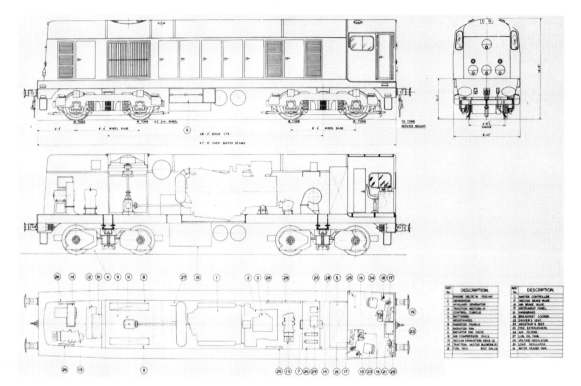

Fig B. A very interesting Type 3 proposal using the BR Class 20 Bo-Bo design to take the Deltic 18 engine to produce a 1700hp 72-ton locomotive in 1957. (*GEC Traction Ltd*)

for batches of 50 locomotives and it is worth noting that the Deltic 9 engine was offered at 1250hp, and the Deltic 18 at 2500hp in supercharged form. The locomotives were more than competitive with the WR Warship class B-B diesel-hydraulics of Classes 42 and 43.

Moving on to the 1965–7 period and the so-called 'Super Deltic' which was in fact produced in three designs (along with alternatives with up-rated EE conventional engines, EE-Sulzer engines, and the French AGO engine), the Deltic-engined locomotives all had two 18-cylinder engines each rated at 2000hp in two designs, and at 2300hp in a third, giving in this case 4600hp for a service weight of 114 tons – less than the Class 47! All three were similar to the coming Class 50 2700hp EE locomotives for BR so far as the mechanical design was concerned, the two 4000hp versions weighing 117 tons and all three being of Co-Co layout. BR considered costs for batches of twenty and fifty.

Investment on such locomotives could have provided a machine for 24 hours per day use on a variety of work, not being constrained by fixed-consist train sets, this alternative appealing to some people in BR. The HST train sets with their 2250hp lightweight power cars do nevertheless have the advantage of providing plenty of power with low axle loadings. It has been expressed by protagonists of the Deltic engine that the HSTs should have been Deltic-powered instead of having the Paxman Valenta, but nothing documentary can be offered to support this story.

At the time of writing, the end of the Deltic locomotive is hoving into view and, sadly, I feel certain that its like will never be seen again. The National Railway Museum is preserving a Class 55 in working order and the Deltic Preservation Society (DPS) has a similarly worthwhile aim in view, deserving all the support that it can muster. The retention of two, or hopefully more, of these locomotives will enable future enthusiasts, engineers and the general public to witness the amazing effect of these worldbeaters at work.

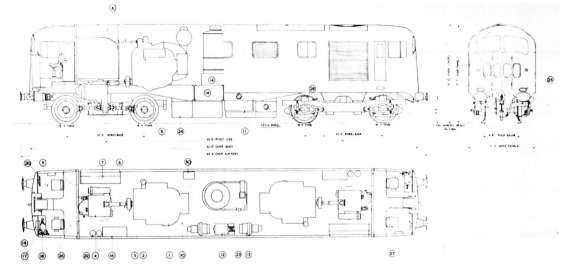

Fig C. Only a rather faded original drawing was available to illustrate this proposal for the Western Region of BR – a diesel-hydraulic locomotive using two Deltic 9-cylinder engines and Stone–Mekhydro hydro-mechanical transmission. With two 850hp engines the result was a 1700hp B-B locomotive weighing 74 tons. (*GEC Traction Ltd*)

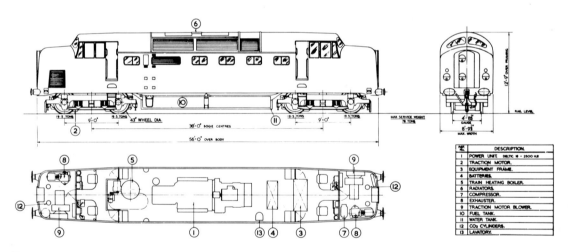

Ref. No.	DESCRIPTION.
1	POWER UNIT. DELTIC 18 - 2500 H.P.
2	TRACTION MOTOR.
3	EQUIPMENT FRAME.
4	BATTERIES.
5	TRAIN HEATING BOILER.
6	RADIATORS.
7	COMPRESSOR.
8	EXHAUSTER.
9	TRACTION MOTOR BLOWER.
10	FUEL TANK.
11	WATER TANK.
12	CO_2 CYLINDERS.
13	LAVATORY.

Fig D. Four variants on this Bo-Bo diesel-electric in the 72-ton to 79-ton range and with either Deltic 18 or a pair of Deltic 9 engines were proposed in 1958, with steam or electric train-heating. The 78-ton 2500hp example above had steam heating. (*GEC Traction Ltd*)

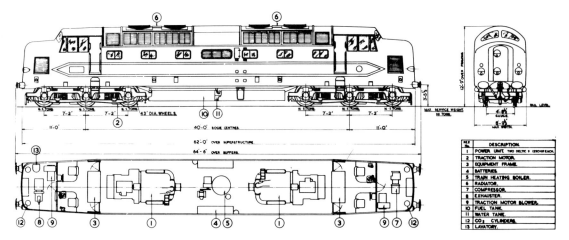

Fig E. With a definite similarity to the prototype *Deltic* design, this 96- or 99-ton Co-Co with two Deltic 9 or one Deltic 18 engine was a predecessor of the thinking leading to British Rail's desire for more powerful Type 4 diesels of at least 2500hp, culminating in the Class 47. The twin-engine version illustrated was proposed in 1958. (*GEC Traction Ltd*)

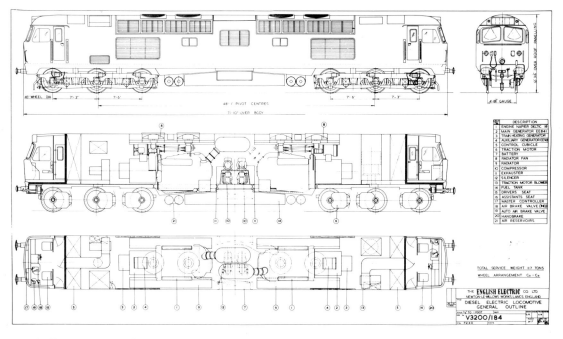

Fig F. The abortive 'Super-Deltic' proposals of 1965–7 offering 4400/4600hp Co-Co locomotives of as little as 114 tons weight was most promising. However, the courage to go ahead with further Deltic locomotives on BR was not apparent at the time. The one illustrated is of 117 tons weight and has electric train heating. (*GEC Traction Ltd*)

TABLE LISTING THE PRINCIPAL DETAILS OF THE SIX PROPOSED DELTIC DESIGNS COVERED IN CHAPTER 10

	Fig. A	Fig. B	Fig. C	Fig. D	Fig. E	Fig. F
Axle layout	Bo-Bo	Bo-Bo	B-B	Bo-Bo	Co-Co	Co-Co
Length over body	50ft 0in	—	52ft 0in	56ft 0in	62ft 0in	71ft 10in
Length over buffer beams	—	47ft 0in	—	—	—	—
Bogie wheelbase	8ft 6in	8ft 6in	10ft 6in	9ft 0in	14ft 4in	14ft 9in
Bogie pivots	32ft 0in	28ft 0in	32ft 0in	38ft 0in	40ft 0in	48ft 1in
Height	12ft 0in	12ft 8in	12ft 8in	12ft 9in	12ft 9in	12ft 9$^1/_{16}$in
Width	8ft 10$\frac{3}{4}$in	8ft 10in	9ft 0in	8ft 9$\frac{1}{2}$in	8ft 9$\frac{1}{2}$in	—
Weight in working order	72Tons	72Tons	74Tons	72/76/78Tons	96/99Tons	117Tons
Engine model	D18–25	D18–25	Two T9–29	D18–25	Two T9–29	Two D18–25
Engine total hp	1700	1700	1700	2500	2500	4400
Wheel diameter	3ft 7in	3ft 7in	3ft 7in	3ft 7in	—	3ft 9in
Train heating type	ETH	ETH	Steam	Steam 78Tons ETH 76Tons ETH(MR) 72Tons	Steam 99Tons ETH 96Tons	ETH

COMPLETE LIST OF DELTIC-ENGINED LOCOMOTIVES WITH MAKERS' NUMBERS, DELIVERY, REGIONAL ALLOCATION WHEN NEW, AND WITHDRAWAL DATES

Locomotive	EE Rotation No	Building works	Building works rotation No	Date into service	Regional allocation	Withdrawn
Deltic	2007	EE Preston	—	10.55	LM+E	3.61
D5900	2377	Vulcan Foundry	D417	22.5.59	E	30.12.68
D5901	2378	Vulcan Foundry	D418	22.5.59	E	7.12.69
D5902	2379	Vulcan Foundry	D419	1.5.59	E	23.11.69
D5903	2380	Vulcan Foundry	D420	17.4.59	E	30.12.68
D5904	2381	Vulcan Foundry	D421	24.4.59	E	20.1.69
D5905	2382	Vulcan Foundry	D422	8.5.59	E	14.2.71
D5906	2383	Vulcan Foundry	D423	8.5.59	E	30.9.68
D5907	2384	Vulcan Foundry	D424	15.5.59	E	20.10.68
D5908	2385	Vulcan Foundry	D425	29.5.59	E	9.3.69
D5909	2386	Vulcan Foundry	D426	19.6.59	E	7.3.71
D9000	2905	Vulcan Foundry	D557	28.2.61	SC	
D9001	2906	Vulcan Foundry	D558	23.2.61	E	6.1.80
D9002	2907	Vulcan Foundry	D559	9.3.61	NE	
D9003	2908	Vulcan Foundry	D560	27.3.61	E	31.12.80
D9004	2909	Vulcan Foundry	D561	18.5.61	SC	
D9005	2910	Vulcan Foundry	D562	25.5.61	NE	2.81
D9006	2911	Vulcan Foundry	D563	29.6.61	SC	2.81
D9007	2912	Vulcan Foundry	D564	22.6.61	E	
D9008	2913	Vulcan Foundry	D565	7.7.61	NE	
D9009	2914	Vulcan Foundry	D566	21.7.61	E	
D9010	2915	Vulcan Foundry	D567	21.7.61	SC	
D9011	2916	Vulcan Foundry	D568	24.8.61	NE	
D9012	2917	Vulcan Foundry	D569	4.9.61	E	5.81
D9013	2918	Vulcan Foundry	D570	14.9.61	SC	
D9014	2919	Vulcan Foundry	D571	29.9.61	NE	
D9015	2920	Vulcan Foundry	D572	13.10.61	E	
D9016	2921	Vulcan Foundry	D573	27.10.61	SC	
D9017	2922	Vulcan Foundry	D574	9.11.61	NE	
D9018	2923	Vulcan Foundry	D575	24.11.61	E	
D9019	2924	Vulcan Foundry	D576	11.12.61	SC	
D9020	2925	Vulcan Foundry	D577	12.2.62	E	6.1.80
D9021	2926	Vulcan Foundry	D578	16.3.62	SC	

EE Contract Numbers
Prototype Deltic   6B2000
Class 23   CCF0875
Class 55   CCK0980

Depot Allocations:
Class 23 Hornsey, then Finsbury Park
Class 55 ER – Finsbury Park
       SCR – Haymarket   NER – Gateshead

COMPARISON OF MAIN DETAILS AND DIMENSIONS OF DELTIC-ENGINED LOCOMOTIVES

	1955 *Deltic*	Class 23	Class 55
Length over buffers	67ft 9in	52ft 6in	69ft 6in
Overall height	12ft 10in	12ft 8in	12ft 10in
Overall width	8ft 9½in	8ft 10¾in	8ft 9½in
Bogie wheelbase	14ft 4in	8ft 6in	13ft 6in
Bogie centres	44ft 0in	32ft 0in	45ft 0in
Wheel diameter	3ft 7in	3ft 7in	3ft 7in
Weight in working order (tons)	106	73·85	99
Maximum axle load (tons)	18·0	18·5	16·5
Continuous tractive effort	29,000lb at 35mph	31,800lb at 10mph	35,000lb at 32mph
Maximum speed (mph)	90 later 105	75	105
Fuel tank capacity (galls)	800	550	900 later 826
Water tank capacity (gallons)	600	500	640 later 830
Main generator type and number fitted	EE 831A (two)	EE 835D (one)	EE 829 (two)
Auxiliary generator type and number fitted	EE 912A (two)	EE 912 (one)	EE 913 (two)
Traction motor type and number fitted	EE 526A (six)	EE 533A (four)	EE 538A (six)
Gear ratio	61:9 later 59:21	62:17	59:21
Steam train-heating generator type	Stone vapor later Clayton	Stone vapor	Spanner MkII
Output of steam (lb/hr)	2000	1750	2000
Total engine hp	3300	1100	3300
Rail hp	2650	768	2640

The end of the Deltic high-speed era. Finsbury Park depot's favourite, 55007 *Pinza*, immaculately turned-out, stands at King's Cross with the last locomotive-hauled down Hull Executive, complete with train nameboard, on 3 January 1981. From 5 January 1981 an HST took over this train. (*Roger Newling-Goode*)

INDEX

(Only principal references are given)